Edexcel Award in
Statistical Methods

Level
3

WORKBOOK

Peter Sherran

LWAYS LEARNING

PEARSON

Published by Pearson Education Limited, Edinburgh Gate, Harlow, Essex, CM20 2JE.

www.pearsonschoolsandfecolleges.co.uk

Text © Pearson Education Limited 2013
Edited by Project One Publishing Solutions, Scotland
Typeset and illustrated by Tech-Set Ltd, Gateshead
Original illustrations © Pearson Education Limited 2013
Cover image © AXL / Shutterstock.com

The right of Peter Sherran to be identified as author of this work has been asserted by him in accordance with the Copyright, Designs and Patents Act 1988.

First published 2013

17 16 15 14 13
10 9 8 7 6 5 4 3 2 1

British Library Cataloguing in Publication Data
A catalogue record for this book is available from the British Library

ISBN 978 1 446 90331 5

Printed in Slovakia by Neografia

Acknowledgements
Every effort has been made to contact copyright holders of material reproduced in this book. Any omissions will be rectified in subsequent printings if notice is given to the publishers.

Disclaimer
This material has been published on behalf of Edexcel and offers high-quality support for the delivery of Edexcel qualifications.

This does not mean that the material is essential to achieve any Edexcel qualification, nor does it mean that it is the only suitable material available to support any Edexcel qualification. Material from this publication will not be used verbatim in any examination or assessment set by Edexcel. Any resource lists produced by Edexcel shall include this and other appropriate resources.

Copies of official specifications for all Edexcel qualifications may be found on the Edexcel website: www.edexcel.com

In the writing of this book, no Edexcel examiners authored sections relevant to examination papers for which they have responsibility.

Notices
The AS links provide references to course books as follows:

S1 Edexcel AS and A Level Modular Mathematics Statistics 1
ISBN 978 0 43551 912 4

Contents

Self-assessment chart

	Needs more practice	Almost there	I'm proficient!	Notes
Chapter 1 Data				
1.1 Collecting and classifying data	☐	☐	☐	
1.2 Calculating a stratified sample using two categories	☐	☐	☐	
1.3 Petersen's capture and recapture method	☐	☐	☐	
Chapter 2 Displaying data				
2.1 Drawing diagrams	☐	☐	☐	
Chapter 3 Calculating with data				
3.1 Means and index numbers	☐	☐	☐	
3.2 Mean and standard deviation for grouped and ungrouped data	☐	☐	☐	
3.3 Outliers	☐	☐	☐	
3.4 Measures of correlation	☐	☐	☐	
3.5 Calculation of S_{xx}, S_{yy} and S_{xy}	☐	☐	☐	
3.6 Calculation of standardised scores	☐	☐	☐	
Chapter 4 Interpreting data				
4.1 Compare histograms and normal distributions	☐	☐	☐	
4.2 Identify and describe correlation in scatter graphs and interpret measures of correlation	☐	☐	☐	
4.3 Identify trend and seasonality in time-series graphs	☐	☐	☐	
4.4 Interpret and compare data	☐	☐	☐	
4.5 Geometric means and chain base index numbers	☐	☐	☐	
4.6 Interpreting diagrams	☐	☐	☐	
Chapter 5 Probability				
5.1 Probability and relative frequency	☐	☐	☐	
5.2 Sample space diagrams and Venn diagrams	☐	☐	☐	
5.3 Tree diagrams	☐	☐	☐	
5.4 Mutually exclusive events	☐	☐	☐	
5.5 Combined events	☐	☐	☐	
5.6 Conditional probabilities	☐	☐	☐	
5.7 Binomial probabilities	☐	☐	☐	
5.8 The normal distribution	☐	☐	☐	

1.1 Collecting and classifying data

AS LINKS
S1: 2.1 Classification of variables

By the end of this section you will know how to:

* Recognise and describe different types of data and methods of collection
* Understand why sampling is used

Key points

* A **population** is a complete collection of people, creatures or objects from which data may be collected for an enquiry.
* A **sampling frame** is a **list** of the members of the population.
* A **sample** is chosen from the sampling frame to represent the population.
* In a **census**, data is collected from every member of the population.
* **Discrete data** can only take specific values.
* **Continuous data** can take any numerical value in a given range.
* **Categorical data** may be sorted into different categories.
* **Quantitative variables** involve numbers for counting or measuring.
* **Qualitative variables** involve descriptions without numbers.
* **Primary data** is collected directly by the researcher.
* **Secondary data** is used by the researcher but collected by someone else.

Census, population and sampling frames

1 A large hotel has rooms for over 2000 guests. Josephine manages the Reception and wants to know what the guests think about the new check-in system. She decides to ask a sample of the guests.

   a Describe a sampling frame that Josephine could use.

     ....

> **Hint**
> The sampling frame is a list.

   b Write down one advantage of taking a sample.

     ....

     ....

> **Hint**
> Consider how long it would take to ask all of the guests.

2 A television ratings company surveys a sample audience to work out which television programmes are most popular in the Yorkshire Television area.

   a Describe a suitable sampling frame for this survey.

     ....

   b Explain why a sample is taken rather than a census.

     ....

     ....

3 An examiner marks around 500 exam papers. A lead examiner selects a sample of these papers and re-marks them to check that the papers have been marked consistently.

   a Describe the sampling frame.

     ....

   b Explain why a sample is taken rather than a census.

     ....

     ....

4 Jack wants to find out if people prefer to read ebooks or paper books.
He is going to take a sample of the students at his university.

a Describe a suitable sampling frame.

....

....

b Give one advantage of taking a sample rather than a census.

....

....

c Describe a situation where it is important to take a census rather than a sample, and explain why.

....

....

....

Types of data

Hint
Consider whether the variable can take any value in a given range.

Guided

5 a Is shoe size an example of a discrete variable or a continuous variable?
Explain your answer.

....

....

....

b Is foot length an example of a discrete variable or a continuous variable? Explain your answer.

....

....

....

Practice

6 Fill in the missing words.

a A variable found by measuring is a .... variable.

b A variable found by counting is a .... variable.

7 Here are some variables that may be used to describe a car.

A Seating capacity   **B** Colour   **C** Weight   **D** Fuel tank capacity   **E** Make

Write each of the letters A, B C, D and E in the appropriate circle to show the type of variable it represents.

Qualitative   Discrete   Continuous

8 Complete the table by ticking the correct box in each row.

Variable	Variable type	
	Qualitative	Quantitative
The lap times of a driver in a Formula 1 race		
The names of the drivers in a Formula 1 race		
The number of people in a swimming pool		
The distance between two ships		
The colour of an iron bar as it is heated		

Primary and secondary data

9 Describe the data collected in these examples as primary data or secondary data.

a Jasmine measures the heights of all the students in her class.

....

> **Hint**
> Jasmine does the measuring herself.

b Ted collects information from the internet about average monthly temperatures in the UK over the last five years.

....

> **Hint**
> Ted relies on another source for his information.

c John is doing an experiment to find out if a dice is biased. He throws the dice 60 times and records the scores.

....

> **Hint**
> John records his own results for the experiment.

10 Complete the table by ticking the correct box in each row.

Data	Data type	
	Primary	Secondary
Processor speeds from a computer magazine		
Answers to a survey that you conduct		
The amount of time you spend watching television in one week		
Information about the number of horses used in the First World War		
Published league tables of exam results		

11 Kelly works for a drugs company. She wants to find out about the effectiveness of a new flu vaccine.

a Would you expect her to use primary data or secondary data?

....

b Explain your answer to part **a**.

....

....

1.2 Calculating a stratified sample using two categories

By the end of this section you will know how to:

✳ Calculate the size of a stratified sample using two categories

Key points

✳ The population may be divided into groups using two categories.

✳ A **stratified sample** contains members of every group in proportion to the size of the group.

✳ The number of members of a group taken as part of a stratified sample is given by

$$\frac{\text{Group size}}{\text{Population size}} \times \text{Sample size}$$

Guided

1　The two-way table gives information about the numbers of members of a sports club.

	Membership type		Total
	Premium	**Standard**	
Male	16	24	40
Female	14	21	35
Total	30	45	75

Jess wants to take a sample of 20 members stratified by gender and by membership type. Work out the number of females with Standard membership in her sample.

Group size = ...

> **Hint**
> Look in the Female row for the number in the Standard column.

Population size = ...

> **Hint**
> This is the total number of members.

> **Hint**
> This is the number of people chosen for the sample.

Sample size = ...

Number of females with Standard membership in the sample = $\dfrac{..........}{..........} \times ....$

$= ....$

$= ....$

> **Hint**
> Substitute the values you have found into the formula.

> **Hint**
> Round your final answer to the nearest whole number.

2 A company produces coats for dogs. The coats are made in three sizes and in two different colours. The table gives information about the numbers of coats made in one day.

	Small	Medium	Large
Blue	34	85	21
Brown	38	92	29

A sample of 30 coats is taken, stratified by size and by colour.
Find the number of large blue coats in the sample.

....

3 A theatre has three types of seating available for matinee and evening performances. The table gives information about the numbers of seats used on one day.

Performance	Front stalls	Rear stalls	Circle
Matinee	188	146	134
Evening	196	284	223

A sample of 50 audience members stratified by performance and by type of seating is taken.
Find how many people in the sample had a seat in the Circle for the matinee performance.

....

4 The table gives information about the numbers of students in Years 7, 8 and 9.

	Year 7	Year 8	Year 9
Boys	186	178	174
Girls	194	172	185

A sample of 40 pupils stratified by year and by gender is to be taken.
Work out the number of Year 8 girls in the sample.

....

5 A bakery has four ovens A, B, C and D. Each oven produces two batches of cakes per day. The table gives information about the numbers of cakes produced.

	Oven			
	A	**B**	**C**	**D**
Batch 1	64	72	55	84
Batch 2	58	70	58	76

A sample of 30 cakes stratified by oven and by batch is to be taken.
Work out the number of cakes from Batch 1 of oven A in the sample.

....

1.3 Petersen's capture and recapture method

By the end of this section you will know how to:

* Use the capture–recapture method to estimate the size of a population

Key points

* The **Petersen's capture and recapture** method is used to estimate the size of a population by sampling.
* A **sample** of the population is taken.
* The sample is counted and **marked** in a way that can be identified later.
* The sample is **returned** to the population and then a **second sample** is taken at **random**.
* The second sample is counted and the number of these that are found to be marked is counted.
* An **estimate** of the size of the population is given by the formula

$$N = \frac{Mn}{m}$$

In the formula:
  N is the estimated size of the population
  M is the number first captured and marked
  n is the size of the second sample
  m is the number in the second sample found to have been previously marked.

* Some key assumptions on which the reliability of the method depends are:
  * the original sample disperses **evenly** into the population
  * the population has a **fixed size** for the time between the samples being taken
  * the marks used are not lost and remain recognisable
  * every member of the population has an equal chance of being captured.

Guided

1 A sample of 20 fish is caught in a small pond. The fish are tagged and returned to the pond. Two days later a second sample of 21 fish is caught, and 3 of these are found to have been tagged.

a Estimate the number of fish in the pond.

$M = $ ....
> **Hint**
> M is the number of fish caught and tagged in the first sample.

$n = $ ....
> **Hint**
> n is the number of fish caught in the second sample.

$m = $ ....
> **Hint**
> m is the number of fish in the second sample that have been tagged.

Using the formula $N = \frac{Mn}{m}$ $N = \dfrac{\text{............} \times \text{............}}{\text{............}}$

An estimate for the number of fish in the pond is ....

b Explain the purpose of waiting two days before taking the second sample.

....

....

> **Hint**
> Check the key assumptions on which this method relies.

Practice

2 100 gannets were captured at a gannet sanctuary. The birds were tagged and returned to the sanctuary. A second sample of 96 gannets contained 4 birds that had been tagged in the first sample.

a Estimate the number of gannets in the gannet sanctuary.

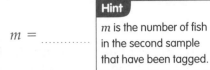

....

b State two assumptions made in making your estimate.

1 ....

2 ....

3 Kerry wants to estimate the number of beads in a large jar. She takes out 50 beads and marks them with a pen. She returns the marked beads to the jar and mixes them in. Kerry then takes out another 40 beads at random and finds that 3 of the beads are marked.

a Use this information to work out an estimate of the number of beads in the jar.

....

b Explain why Kerry mixed in the marked beads before selecting the second sample.

....

....

Don't forget!

✳ A sampling frame is a .... of the members of the population.

✳ A sample is chosen from the sampling frame to .... the population.

✳ In a census, data is collected from .... of the population.

✳ Discrete data can only take ....

✳ Continuous data can take any numerical value in ....

✳ Quantitative variables involve numbers for counting or ....

✳ Qualitative variables involve .... without numbers.

✳ Secondary data is used by the researcher but collected by ....

✳ A stratified sample contains members of every group in .... to the size of the group.

✳ The number of members of a group taken as part of a stratified sample is given by

$$\frac{\text{Group size}}{\text{Population size}} \times \text{...}$$

✳ In the capture–recapture method, an estimate of the size of the population is given by

$$N = \frac{Mn}{m}$$

In the formula:

N is the .... of the population

M is the number first .... and ....

n is the size of the .... sample

m is the number in the second sample found to have been ....

✳ Some key assumptions on which the reliability of the method depends are:

• the original sample .... into the population

• the population has a fixed .... for the time between the samples being taken

• the .... or .... used are not lost and remain recognisable

• every member of the population has an .... of being caught.

Exam-style questions

1 A proposal has been made for a new high-speed train line to be built within five miles of a village. William wants to know how this will affect people in the village.

   a Describe a sampling frame that William could use.

   ....

   ....

   b Give one example of using a sample.

   ....

   ....

   c Give one example of using a census.

   ....

   ....

2 Alice and Bob are at a tennis match.
   Alice records whether each serve is in, or is a let, or is out.
   Bob records the speed of each serve.
   Choose from the words

Discrete	Qualitative	Continuous

   to answer these questions.

   a What type of data does Alice collect?   ....

   b What type of data does Bob collect?   ....

3 Students at a college follow a main course in Art, Humanities or Science.
   The table gives information about the numbers of students on these courses.

	Course		
	Art	**Humanities**	**Science**
Male	124	105	148
Female	132	96	137

   A sample of 40 students stratified by course and by gender is to be taken.
   Calculate the number of female science students in the sample.

   ....

4 A sample of 100 trout is taken from a trout farm. The fish are marked and returned.
   A second sample of 75 trout is taken and 5 of these fish have been marked.

   a Work out an estimate of the number of trout in the trout farm.

   ....

   b Give one reason for using this method instead of counting all of the fish directly.

   ....

   ....

2.1 Drawing diagrams

AS LINKS
S1: Chapter 4 Representation of data; Section 5.2 Solving probability problems by drawing Venn diagrams

By the end of this section you will know how to:

* draw back-to-back stem and leaf diagrams
* draw box plots with outliers using cumulative frequency graphs
* draw histograms with unequal class intervals
* sketch normal distributions
* complete Venn diagrams

Key points

* A **back-to-back stem and leaf diagram** can be used to compare two data distributions.
* Information from a **cumulative frequency diagram**, together with information about the maximum and minimum values, may be used to draw a **box plot**.
* **Histograms** with **unequal** class intervals show **frequency density** on the vertical axis.
* A **normal distribution curve** is symmetrical about the mean. 99.8% of the data values lie within 3 **standard deviations** of the mean.
* A **Venn diagram** may be used to represent a sample space.

Stem and leaf diagrams

1 Here are the heights of 30 Year 11 students in centimetres.

Boys

181	185	176	180	181	172	183	167
177	189	170	175	193	182	179	184

Girls

169	163	168	172	157	166	170
157	162	167	171	183	178	169

> **Hint**
> It's a good idea to put a line through each result as you write it on the diagram.

Draw an ordered back-to-back stem and leaf diagram for this information.

Boys		Girls
	15	7 7
7	16	2
2 0	17	
	18	
	19	

> **Hint**
> The results for the girls are ordered from left to right. The results for the boys are ordered from right to left.

Key: 7 | 16 | 2 represents 167 cm for the boys and ....

> **Hint**
> You must include a key for both sides of the diagram.

2 20 students took two maths papers. Here are the results.

Paper 1

58	62	51	76	69	75	72	63	59	70
64	48	59	68	43	82	74	87	55	66

Paper 2

46	57	60	68	55	73	73	64	71	68
61	52	44	77	82	80	75	63	50	49

Paper 1		Paper 2
	4	
	5	
	6	
	7	
	8	

Draw an ordered back-to-back stem and leaf diagram for this information. You must include a key.

3 Here are the heights of some ponies and horses, measured in hands.

Ponies

13.2	12.1	12.0	14.1	13.2	12.3	14.2
14.1	13.0	14.2	13.3	14.3	12.2	13.1

Horses

15.3	15.1	14.3	16.2	14.2	16.3	16.1
14.2	15.0	15.3	16.1	14.3	16.2	14.3

Draw an ordered back-to-back stem and leaf diagram to represent this information.
You must include a key.

Ponies		Horses
	12	
	13	
	14	
	15	
	16	

Box plots

4 The table shows some information about the distances thrown d, in metres, in a javelin competition.

41.4 m is the only outlier for the distribution.
The shortest distance that is not an outlier is 44.6 m.
On the grid, draw a box plot to show this information.

	Distance (d metres)
Shortest	41.4
Lower quartile	51.8
Median	56.4
Upper quartile	58.2
Longest	59.8

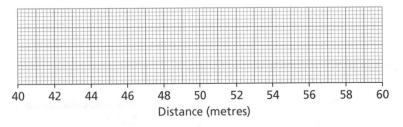

Distance (metres)

Hint
An outlier is marked with a cross.

Hint
Draw the rest of the box plot as normal, showing 44.6 m as the shortest distance.

5 The cumulative frequency diagram gives information about the birth weights of 48 babies.

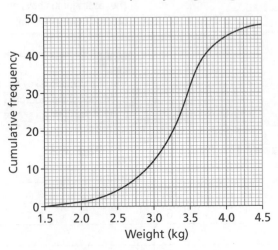

Hint
Use the cumulative frequency graph to find the lower quartile, median and upper quartile.

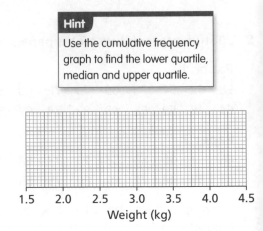

The weight of the lightest baby was 1.9 kg.
The weight of the heaviest baby was 4.3 kg.
On the grid, draw a box plot for this information.

6 The table gives information about the test scores *t* of 50 students.

Test score (*t*)	Frequency	Cumulative frequency
20 < t ≤ 30	1	
30 < t ≤ 40	5	
40 < t ≤ 50	9	
50 < t ≤ 60	12	
60 < t ≤ 70	14	
70 < t ≤ 80	7	
80 < t ≤ 90	2	

On the grid, draw a cumulative frequency graph for this information.
The first three points have been plotted for you.

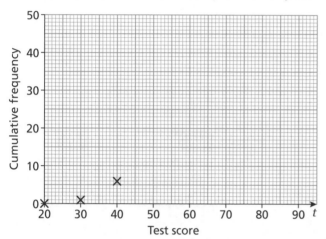

Hint
Plot all the points before sketching the curve.

The lowest test score was 24.
The highest test score was 88.
On the grid, draw a box plot for this information.

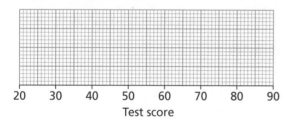

7 The amounts of tax paid in one month by 23 employees of a company are shown in the stem and leaf diagram. Each amount has been rounded to the nearest £10.

Key: 3 | 7 means £370

```
2 │ 2  6  8  8
3 │ 1  5  5  7  8
4 │ 2  2  2 · 3  6  7  7  8
5 │ 3  8  9  9
6 │ 2  2
```

On the grid, draw a box plot to show this information.

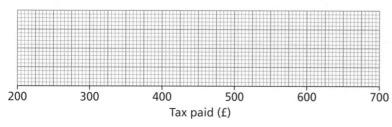

Histograms with unequal class intervals

Guided

8 The table gives information about the wingspans w, in centimetres, of 100 bats.

Wingspan (w cm)	Frequency	Frequency density
$15 < w \leqslant 20$	10	2
$20 < w \leqslant 25$	40	8
$25 < w \leqslant 30$	25	
$30 < w \leqslant 40$	15	1.5
$40 < w \leqslant 60$	10	

Hint
Notice that the class widths vary.

On the grid, draw a histogram for this information.

$$\text{Frequency density} = \frac{\text{Frequency}}{\text{Class width}}$$

$$\frac{10}{5} = 2 \qquad \frac{40}{5} = 8 \qquad \frac{15}{10} = 1.5$$

Hint
The class interval $30 < w \leqslant 40$ has width 10.

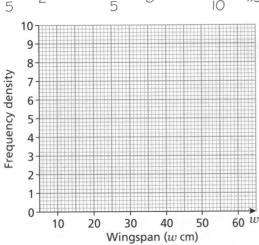

Hint
Leave no gaps between the bars.

Hint
The height of each bar is the frequency density.

Practice

9 The table gives information about the times t taken by 30 different objects to fall 10 m under gravity.

Time (t seconds)	Frequency	Frequency density
$1.4 < t \leqslant 1.5$	14	
$1.5 < t \leqslant 1.6$	9	
$1.6 < t \leqslant 1.7$	3	
$1.7 < t \leqslant 1.9$	4	

On the grid, draw a histogram for this information.

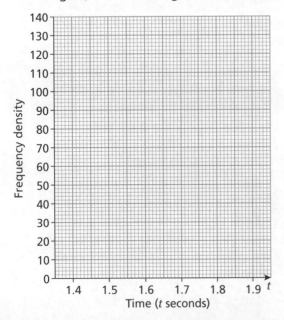

10 The table gives information about the heights h, in millimetres, of 50 seedlings.

Height (h mm)	Frequency
$0 < h \leqslant 15$	3
$15 < h \leqslant 20$	11
$20 < h \leqslant 25$	19
$25 < h \leqslant 30$	12
$30 < h \leqslant 40$	5

On the grid, draw a histogram for this information.

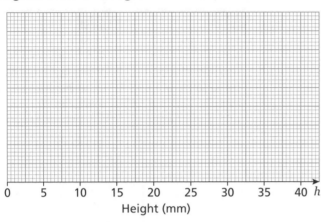

Height (mm)

Normal distributions

11 The heights of some students may be modelled by a normal distribution with mean 175 cm and standard deviation 7 cm. The heights of 84.1% of students are less than 182 cm.
Label and shade the diagram to show this information.

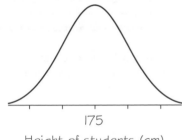

175

Height of students (cm)

Hint
Draw a vertical line corresponding to a height of 182 cm.

Hint
Shade the area under the curve representing a height of less than 182 cm.

Hint
Indicate that the shaded area represents 84.1% of students.

Hint
Each interval on the horizontal scale represents one standard deviation. Label each of the points on the horizontal scale.

12 The lengths of wooden rails produced by machine may be modelled by a normal distribution with mean 216.5 cm and standard deviation 0.1 cm. The lengths of 97.7% of the rails are greater than 216.3 cm.
Label and shade the diagram to show this information.

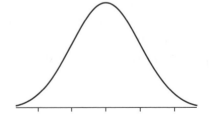

13 The lifetime of some batteries is normally distributed with mean 30 hours and standard deviation 1.5 hours. The lifetimes of 68.2% of the batteries are between 28.5 hours and 31.5 hours.
Label and shade the diagram to show this information.

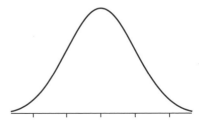

Venn diagrams

14 28 students study both maths and physics in a sixth form.
12 students study maths but not physics.
31 students study physics.
There are 76 students in the sixth form.
Show this information on the Venn diagram.

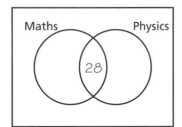

15 There are 35 cars for sale at a garage.
21 of the cars have air-conditioning.
11 of the cars have heated front seats.
9 of the cars do not have either air-conditioning or heated front seats.
Find the number of cars that have both air-conditioning and heated front seats.

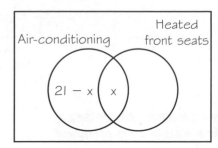

Let x represent the number of cars that have both air-conditioning and heated front seats.

The number of cars with air-conditioning only is $21 - x$

The number of cars with heated front seats only is ....

The total number of cars in the circles is ....

$21 - x + x +$ .... $=$ ....

$$x = ...$$

16 There are 29 stalls at a Farmers' Market.
18 of the stalls sell meat.
14 of the stalls sell vegetables.
5 of the stalls do not sell either meat or vegetables.
Complete the Venn diagram to show this information.

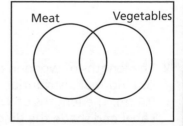

Don't forget!

✳ A back-to-back stem and leaf diagram can be used to .... two data distributions.

✳ Information from a cumulative frequency diagram, together with information about the .... and .... values, may be used to draw a box plot.

✳ Histograms with unequal class intervals show .... on the vertical axis.

✳ A normal distribution curve is symmetrical about the ....

✳ A Venn diagram may be used to represent a ....

Exam-style questions

1 The fuel efficiencies of some petrol cars and some diesel cars were measured in miles per litre. Here are the results.

Petrol

10.2	11.1	9.4	8.7	10.6	9.3	9.4
8.5	10.6	9.6	10.2	8.8	9.6	10.0

Diesel

11.2	10.8	9.8	11.4	12.6	11.8	10.1
10.7	12.2	11.0	12.5	10.7	9.6	11.9

Draw an ordered back-to-back stem and leaf diagram to represent this information. You must include a key.

Petrol		Diesel
	8	
	9	
	10	
	11	
	12	

2 The table shows some information about the times *t* taken by a group of runners to complete a 400 m hurdles race.

	Time (*t* seconds)
Quickest	59.6
Lower quartile	61.1
Median	62.5
Upper quartile	64.3
Slowest	70.4

70.4 seconds is the only outlier for the distribution.
The slowest time that is not an outlier is 65.8 seconds.
On the grid, draw a box plot to show this information.

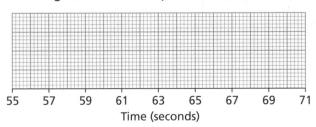

55   57   59   61   63   65   67   69   71
Time (seconds)

3 The table gives information about test results for Year 11 students in a school.

Score (x %)	Frequency
$20 < x \leqslant 40$	12
$40 < x \leqslant 50$	38
$50 < x \leqslant 60$	52
$60 < x \leqslant 70$	41
$70 < x \leqslant 100$	18

On the grid, draw a histogram for this information.

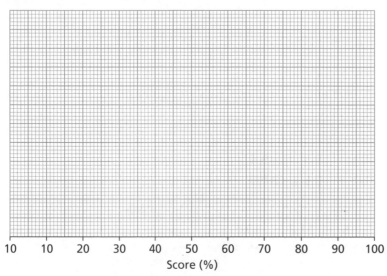

Score (%)

4 The IQ scores of a large group of students were found to be normally distributed with a mean of 100 and a standard deviation of 15.
84.1% of the students had an IQ greater than 85.
Complete the diagram to show this information.

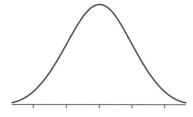

5 An adventure holiday company offers holidays in 20 different locations.
11 of the locations include rock climbing.
6 of the locations include canoeing.
5 of the locations do not include rock climbing and do not include canoeing.
Complete the Venn diagram to show this information.

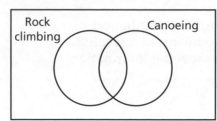

3.1 Means and index numbers

By the end of this section you will know how to:

* Calculate geometric means
* Calculate mean seasonal variation
* Calculate moving base index numbers

Key points

* The **geometric mean** of n numbers $x_1, x_2, x_3, \ldots, x_n$ is given by $\sqrt[n]{(x_1 x_2 x_3 \ldots x_n)}$

* On a time-series graph, the **trend line** is the line of best fit drawn through the plotted moving averages.

* **Seasonal variation** is the difference between the plotted value and the trend line for any selected quarter.

* The **mean seasonal variation**, for a quarter, is the arithmetic mean of the seasonal variations for that quarter.

* A **moving base index number** shows how the price of something changes from one year to the next.

* Moving base index number $= \dfrac{\text{Price in a given year}}{\text{Price in previous year}} \times 100$

1 Calculate the geometric mean of these numbers.

   a 25 and 36

$$\text{Geometric mean} = \sqrt{25 \times 36}$$
$$= \sqrt{\ldots\ldots\ldots\ldots}$$
$$= \ldots\ldots\ldots\ldots\ldots$$

> **Hint**
> There are two numbers so you should find the **square root** of their product.

   b 24, 18 and 4

> **Hint**
> There are three numbers, so you should find the **cube root** of their product.

....

2 Calculate the geometric mean of 120, 132 and 125.
Give your answer correct to 1 decimal place.

....

3 Calculate the geometric mean of these base index numbers: 112, 146, 128 and 156.
Give your answer correct to 1 decimal place.

....

Guided

4 The time-series graph gives information about the number of tablet PCs sold by a shop in each quarter from 2011 to 2012.
The diagram also shows the four-point moving averages and the trend line.

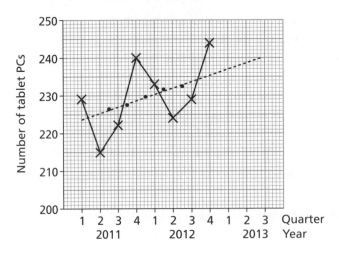

a Find an estimate of the seasonal variation for Quarter 2 in 2011.

2011   Quarter 2   actual value − trend value = 215 − 225 = ...

b Find an estimate of the seasonal variation for Quarter 2 in 2012.

2012   Quarter 2   actual value − trend value = 224 − .... = ...

c Find an estimate of the mean seasonal variation for Quarter 2.

$$\text{Mean seasonal variation for Quarter 2} = \frac{.......... + ...}{2} = ...$$

You should know

Exam questions include the use of mean seasonal variation to make predictions. This will be covered in Section 4.3.

Hint
Use your answers to parts **a** and **b**.

Practice

5 The time-series graph shows the number of people at a holiday resort in each quarter from 2011 to 2012.

a Find an estimate of the seasonal variation for Quarter 1 in 2011.

....

b Find an estimate of the seasonal variation for Quarter 1 in 2012.

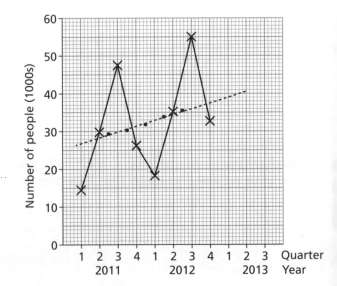

....

c Find an estimate of the mean seasonal variation for Quarter 1.

....

6 The cost of some groceries in January 2011 was £84.20
The cost of the same groceries in January 2012 was £87.60
The cost of the same groceries in January 2013 was £90.45

    a Taking January 2011 as the base year, work out the index number for the cost of the groceries in January 2012.
Give your answer correct to 1 decimal place.

$$\text{Index number} = \frac{\text{Cost in 2012}}{\text{Cost in 2011}} \times 100$$

    ....

    b Taking January 2012 as the base year, work out the index number for the cost of the groceries in January 2013.
Give your answer correct to 1 decimal place.

    ....

    c Interpret and compare the index number for January 2012 with the index number for January 2013.

> **Hint**
> Interpret each index number as a percentage change. Compare the percentage changes.

    ....

    ....

7 Martin is a keen football supporter. The table shows how the price of his season ticket has changed in the last few years.

Year	2011	2012	2013
Price (£)	650	676	710

    a Taking 2011 as the base year, work out the index number for the price of Martin's season ticket in 2012.

    ....

    b Taking 2012 as the base year, work out the index number for the price of Martin's season ticket in 2013.
Give your answer to 1 decimal place.

    ....

    c Interpret and compare the index number for 2012 with the index number for 2013.

    ....

    ....

8   In June 2011 the cost of a package holiday was £1460.
    In June 2012 the cost of a package holiday to the same resort was £1550.
    Between June 2012 and June 2013 the cost of the holiday increased by 6%.

    a   Taking June 2011 as the base year, work out the index number for the cost of the holiday in
    June 2012.
    Give your answer correct to 1 decimal place.

    ....

    b   Taking June 2012 as the base year, work out the index number for the cost of the holiday in
    June 2013.

    ....

    c   Compare the price change from June 2011 to June 2012 with the price change from June 2012
    to June 2013.

    ....

    ....

| Needs more practice | ☐ | Almost there | ☐ | I'm proficient! | ☐ |

3.2   Mean and standard deviation for grouped and ungrouped data

AS LINKS
S1: Chapter 3 Represent
and summary of data

By the end of this section you will know how to:

∗   Calculate the mean and standard deviation of ungrouped data
∗   Calculate the mean and standard deviation of grouped data

Key points

∗   The **standard deviation** for a frequency distribution is given by

$$\sqrt{\frac{\Sigma f x^2}{\Sigma f} - \left(\frac{\Sigma f x}{\Sigma f}\right)^2}$$

∗   In the formula, f is the frequency with which the value x occurs.

∗   The expression inside the square root represents the mean of the squares minus the square of
    the mean.

∗   The same formula may be used for grouped data. In this case, x represents the mid-point of a
    class interval.

Guided

1   Hannah throws a dice 50 times. The table shows her results.

Score (x)	Frequency (f)
1	7
2	5
3	11
4	9
5	10
6	8

Hint
To use the formula, it
helps to add two extra
columns to the table.

Calculate the standard deviation of Hannah's scores.

Score (x)	Frequency (f)	fx	fx²
1	7	7	7
2	5	10	20
3	11	33	99
4	9		
5	10		
6	8		
Total	50		

$\Sigma f = 50$

$\Sigma fx = \ldots\ldots\ldots$

Hint
The total for the third column gives Σfx

$\Sigma fx^2 = \ldots\ldots\ldots$

Hint
The total for the fourth column gives Σfx^2

$\dfrac{\Sigma fx^2}{\Sigma f} - \left(\dfrac{\Sigma fx}{\Sigma f}\right)^2 = \dfrac{\ldots\ldots\ldots}{50} - \left(\dfrac{\ldots\ldots\ldots}{50}\right)^2 = \ldots\ldots\ldots\ldots\ldots$

Standard deviation $= \ldots\ldots\ldots\ldots\ldots$

Hint
The standard deviation is the square root of your last answer.

2 The table gives information about the heights of 60 students.

Height (h cm)	Frequency
$165 < h \leqslant 170$	5
$170 < h \leqslant 175$	12
$175 < h \leqslant 180$	23
$180 < h \leqslant 185$	16
$185 < h \leqslant 190$	4

Hint
This time, three extra columns are needed.

a Calculate an estimate of the mean. Give your answer to 1 decimal place.

Height (h cm)	Frequency (f)	Mid-point (x)	fx	fx²
$165 < h \leqslant 170$	5	167.5	837.5	140 281.25
$170 < h \leqslant 175$	12	172.5	2070	357 075
$175 < h \leqslant 180$	23			
$180 < h \leqslant 185$	16			
$185 < h \leqslant 190$	4			

$\Sigma f = 60$

$\Sigma fx = \ldots\ldots\ldots$

$\dfrac{\Sigma fx}{\Sigma f} = \dfrac{\ldots\ldots\ldots}{60} = \ldots\ldots\ldots\ldots$

An estimate of the mean is $\ldots\ldots\ldots\ldots$ to 1 d.p.

b Calculate an estimate of the standard deviation. Give your answer correct to 1 decimal place.

$\Sigma fx^2 = \ldots\ldots\ldots\ldots\ldots$

$\dfrac{\Sigma fx^2}{\Sigma f} - \left(\dfrac{\Sigma fx}{\Sigma f}\right)^2 = \dfrac{\ldots\ldots\ldots}{60} - \left(\dfrac{\ldots\ldots\ldots}{60}\right)^2 = \ldots\ldots\ldots\ldots\ldots$

An estimate of the standard deviation is $\ldots\ldots\ldots\ldots\ldots$

3 The table gives information about the numbers of goals scored in 30 Premier League football matches.

You are given that $\Sigma fx = 73$ and $\Sigma fx^2 = 235$

a Calculate the mean number of goals scored.

Number of goals, x	Frequency, f
0	3
1	5
2	7
3	8
4	5
5	2

b Calculate the standard deviation of the number of goals scored.

4 The table gives information about the daily amounts of rain in March.

a Calculate an estimate of the mean.

Hours of rain per day, h	Frequency, f
$0 < h \leqslant 2$	12
$2 < h \leqslant 4$	10
$4 < h \leqslant 6$	6
$6 < h \leqslant 8$	3

b Calculate an estimate of the standard deviation.

5 40 students were asked to name as many British Prime Ministers as they could in one minute. The results are shown in the table.

a Calculate the mean.

Number of names, x	Frequency, f
3	5
4	9
5	12
6	10
7	4

b Calculate the standard deviation.

Outliers

3.3

AS LINKS
S1: Section 4.2 Outliers

By the end of this section you will know how to:

∗ Identify outliers

Key points

∗ An **outlier** is an extreme value of the data.
∗ The lower quartile may be written as Q1 and the upper quartile may be written as Q3.
∗ Any data value more than Q3 + 1.5 × IQR is an outlier.
∗ Any data value less than Q1 − 1.5 × IQR is an outlier.

1 Here is some data.

| 18 | 26 | 27 | 27 | 29 | 30 | 31 | 31 | 35 | 40 | 52 |

Identify any outliers.

Position of lower quartile is $\frac{(11 + 1)}{4} = 3$

Lower quartile = QI = ...

Position of upper quartile is $3\frac{(11 + 1)}{4} =$ ....

Upper quartile = Q3 = ...

IQR = ...

Q3 + 1.5 × IQR = ...

QI − 1.5 × IQR = ...

> **Hint**
>
> Any value larger than Q3 + 1.5 × IQR will be an outlier.
>
> Any value smaller than Q1 − 1.5 × IQR will be an outlier.

....

2 Here is some data.

| 16 | 17 | 24 | 42 | 45 | 45 | 46 | 50 | 53 | 56 | 56 | 58 | 60 | 60 | 83 |

a Find the interquartile range.

....

b Identify any outliers.

....

3 Here is some data.

| 18 | 22 | 29 | 36 | 38 | 41 | 42 | 42 | 44 | 46 |
| 47 | 50 | 50 | 51 | 51 | 51 | 58 | 69 | 72 |

Show that 18 and 72 are outliers.

3.4 Measures of correlation

AS LINKS
S1: Chapter 6 Correl

By the end of this section you will know how to:

* Calculate Spearman's coefficient of rank correlation
* Calculate the product-moment correlation coefficient

You should know

Interpretation of the correlation values will be covered in Section 4.2.

Key points

* **Spearman's coefficient of rank correlation** is used to measure the level of agreement between pairs of ranked variables.

* Spearman's coefficient of rank correlation is given by $r_s = 1 - \dfrac{6\Sigma d^2}{n(n^2 - 1)}$

* In the formula, d is the difference in rank for each pair of observations and n is the number of data pairs.

* The **product-moment correlation coefficient** is given by $r = \dfrac{S_{xy}}{\sqrt{S_{xx}S_{yy}}}$

* Formulae or values for S_{xx}, S_{yy} and S_{xy} will be given in the examination but you need to know the formula for r.

Guided

1 Two judges of a diving competition independently gave each of the eight competitors a rank, starting with 1 for the best performer. The table shows the results.

Competitor	Judge 1	Judge 2
A	5	4
B	7	5
C	2	3
D	8	7
E	3	2
F	1	1
G	4	6
H	6	8

Hint

Two extra columns are needed to show the values of d and d^2.

Calculate Spearman's coefficient of rank correlation for this data.

Competitor	Judge 1	Judge 2	d	d^2
A	5	4	1	1
B	7	5	2	4
C	2	3	−1	1
D	8	7	1	1
E	3	2		
F	1	1		
G	4	6		
H	6	8		
			$\Sigma d^2 =$	

$r_s = 1 - \dfrac{6\Sigma d^2}{n(n^2 - 1)} = 1 - \dfrac{6 \times ....}{8(8^2 - 1)}$

Hint

There are 8 competitors, so $n = 8$

$= 1 - \dfrac{}{.............}$

$= ....$ (3 d.p.)

2 Emma and Dan were each asked to rank ten classic cars in a competition.
The table gives information about their rankings.

Car	Emma's rank	Dan's rank
A	6	4
B	3	5
C	4	7
D	1	2
E	8	9
F	10	6
G	7	8
H	9	10
I	2	1
J	5	3

Calculate Spearman's coefficient of rank correlation for this data.

....

3 The table gives information about the total number of goals scored by each of the eight teams in a football competition.
It also shows the teams ranked by their position in the competition.
Team C finished first.

Team	Position	Goals scored
A	3	11
B	5	9
C	1	14
D	4	12
E	8	5
F	6	8
G	2	15
H	7	6

Calculate Spearman's coefficient of rank correlation for this data.

> **Hint**
> It is important to rank the numbers of goals first. Give the highest number of goals rank 1.

....

Guided

4 The table shows the times taken, x minutes, between entering and leaving a supermarket and the amounts spent, £y, by a sample of 10 customers.

Time (x minutes)	15	10	24	16	34	25	18	35	29	31
Amount spent (£y)	23	16	55	11	65	47	25	82	63	70

Given $\quad \Sigma xy = 12\,703 \qquad S_{xx} = 672.1 \qquad S_{yy} = 5698.1$

Use $\qquad S_{xy} = \Sigma xy - \dfrac{\Sigma x \Sigma y}{n}$ and $r = \dfrac{S_{xy}}{\sqrt{S_{yy}S_{xx}}}$

Calculate the product-moment correlation coefficient for this data. Give your answer correct to 2 decimal places.

> **Hint**
> Use the given values for Σx and Σy.

$\Sigma x = 237 \qquad \Sigma y = 457$

$S_{xy} = 12703 - \dfrac{237 \times \ldots\ldots}{10} = \ldots\ldots\ldots\ldots$

$r = \dfrac{\ldots\ldots\ldots}{\sqrt{5698.1 \times \ldots\ldots}} = \dfrac{\ldots\ldots\ldots}{\ldots\ldots\ldots} = \ldots\ldots\ldots\ldots$

Practice

5 The table shows the heights, in metres, and the weights, in kg, of 11 footballers.

Height (x m)	1.77	1.75	1.81	1.90	1.86	1.78	1.83	1.88	1.87	1.91	1.78
Weight (y kg)	72	71	75	83	80	78	74	76	73	80	72

Given $\quad \Sigma xy = 1528.55 \qquad S_{xx} = 0.031\,691 \qquad S_{yy} = 155.6364$

Use $\qquad S_{xy} = \Sigma xy - \dfrac{\Sigma x \Sigma y}{n}$

Calculate the product-moment correlation coefficient for this data. Give your answer correct to 2 decimal places.

> **You should know**
> You need to remember the formula for r.

Step into AS

6 The table gives information about the marks obtained by a group of 10 students in a mock exam and in the actual exam.

Given $\quad \Sigma xy = 38\,894$

$\qquad\quad S_{xx} = 1752.5$

$\qquad\quad S_{yy} = 1728.1$

Use $\qquad S_{xy} = \Sigma xy - \dfrac{\Sigma x \Sigma y}{n}$

Calculate the product-moment correlation coefficient for this data. Give your answer correct to 2 decimal places.

Mock exam mark, x	Actual exam mark, y
68	72
55	39
72	75
45	68
58	65
64	66
82	87
51	55
34	48
66	58

3.5 Calculation of S_{xx}, S_{yy} and S_{xy}

AS LINKS

S1: Chapter 6 Correlation

By the end of this section you will know how to:

* Calculate the values of S_{xx}, S_{yy} and S_{xy}

Key points

* S_{xx} is shorthand for $\Sigma(x - \bar{x})^2$
* Calculation of S_{xx} is made easier by using $S_{xx} = \Sigma x^2 - \dfrac{(\Sigma x)^2}{n}$
* S_{yy} is shorthand for $\Sigma(y - \bar{y})^2$
* Calculation of S_{yy} is made easier by using $S_{yy} = \Sigma y^2 - \dfrac{(\Sigma y)^2}{n}$
* S_{xy} is shorthand for $\Sigma(x - \bar{x})(y - \bar{y})$
* Calculation of S_{xy} is made easier by using $S_{xy} = \Sigma xy - \dfrac{\Sigma x \Sigma y}{n}$

1 A spring is secured at one end and hangs vertically. Ten different weights, w kg, are attached to the free end of the spring and the extension, x cm, is measured each time.
Here is a summary of the results.

$\Sigma w = 32.5$ $\Sigma x = 54.5$ $\Sigma w^2 = 126.25$ $\Sigma x^2 = 355.09$ $\Sigma wx = 211.7$

You may use $S_{xx} = \Sigma x^2 - \dfrac{(\Sigma x)^2}{n}$ and $S_{xy} = \Sigma xy - \dfrac{\Sigma x \Sigma y}{n}$

a Calculate S_{xx}

$S_{xx} = 355.09 - \dfrac{54.5^2}{\dots\dots\dots}$

$= \dots\dots\dots\dots\dots\dots\dots$

> **Hint**
> There are ten observations.

b Calculate S_{ww}

> **Hint**
> Use the formula for S_{xx} but replace x with w.

$\dots\dots\dots\dots\dots\dots$

c Calculate S_{wx}

> **Hint**
> Use the formula for S_{xy} but replace x with w and y with x.

$\dots\dots\dots\dots\dots\dots$

2 In an experiment, an amount of gas was held inside a container.
The gas was maintained at constant temperature. The pressure, p, was measured in response to changing the volume, v, of the container. Ten pairs of readings were taken.
Here is a summary of the results.

$\Sigma v = 275$ $\Sigma p = 424$ $\Sigma p^2 = 33\,482$ $\Sigma v^2 = 9625$ $\Sigma pv = 7085$

You may use $S_{xx} = \Sigma x^2 - \dfrac{(\Sigma x)^2}{n}$ and $S_{xy} = \Sigma xy - \dfrac{\Sigma x \Sigma y}{n}$

a Calculate S_{vv}

....

b Calculate S_{pp}

....

c Calculate S_{pv}

....

3 Tim dropped a stone from different heights, h metres, and found the time taken, t seconds, for the stone to reach the ground each time.
The table gives information about Tim's results.

Height (h m)	Time (t s)	
2.0	0.64	
2.5	0.72	
3.0	0.76	
3.5	0.83	
4.0	0.91	
4.5	0.95	
5.0	1.00	

$\Sigma h^2 = 92.75$ $\Sigma t^2 = 4.9251$

You may use $S_{xx} = \Sigma x^2 - \dfrac{(\Sigma x)^2}{n}$ and $S_{xy} = \Sigma xy - \dfrac{\Sigma x \Sigma y}{n}$

Calculate the product-moment correlation coefficient.

....

Calculation of standardised scores

3.6

By the end of this section you will know how to:

* Use the mean and standard deviation to standardise a score

You should know

Interpretation of standardised scores will be covered in Section 4.4.

Key points

* Standardised score = $\dfrac{\text{Score} - \text{Mean}}{\text{Standard deviation}}$

1 Martin scores 78 marks in a test. The mean mark for the test is 55 and the standard deviation is 10.5
Work out Martin's standardised score.

Standardised score = $\dfrac{\text{Score} - \text{Mean}}{\text{Standard deviation}}$

$$= \frac{78 - \text{..........}}{10.5} = \text{..........................}$$

$$= \text{..........................} \text{ (1 d.p.)}$$

2 The number of patients treated at an accident and emergency of a hospital on Saturday nights has mean 35 and standard deviation 3.6
On one particular Saturday only 29 patients were treated.
Work out the standardised score for this number of patients.

....

3 The mean number of strokes required to complete a golf course is 95 and the standard deviation is 6.4
The table shows Tim's score on each hole.

Hole	1	2	3	4	5	6	7	8	9	10	11	12	13	14	15	16	17	18
Score	4	5	4	3	6	5	5	6	7	5	4	6	8	9	7	7	8	9

Work out Tim's standardised score.

....

Don't forget!

* The geometric mean of four numbers a, b, c and d is given by ....

* On a time-series graph, the trend line is the line of .... drawn through the plotted moving averages.

* The mean seasonal variation, for a quarter, is the arithmetic mean of the variations from the .... for that quarter.

* The standard deviation for a frequency distribution is given by $\sqrt{\dfrac{\Sigma......}{\Sigma f} - \left(\dfrac{\Sigma fx}{\Sigma f}\right)^2}$

* The same formula may be used for grouped data. In this case, x represents the .... of a class interval.

* A data value more than 1.5 times the IQR above the .... is an outlier.

* A data value more than 1.5 times the IQR below the .... is an outlier.

* Spearman's coefficient of rank correlation is given by $r_s = 1 - \dfrac{6\Sigma......^2}{n(n^2 - 1)}$

* The product-moment correlation coefficient is given by $r = \dfrac{......}{\sqrt{S_{xx}S_{yy}}}$

* .... is shorthand for $\Sigma(x - \bar{x})(y - \bar{y})$

* Standardised score $= \dfrac{\text{Score} - ......}{\text{Standard deviation}}$

Exam-style questions

1 Stacy likes to rent a villa for her holidays.
   The table shows how much she paid in 2011, 2012 and in 2013.

Year	2011	2012	2013
Rental (£)	580	612	720

   a Taking 2011 as the base year, work out the index number for the rent that Stacy paid in 2012. Give your answer to 1 decimal place.

   b Taking 2012 as the base year, work out the index number for the rent that Stacy paid in 2013. Give your answer to 1 decimal place.

2 The table gives information about the distances, in miles, that students in one class travel to get to school.

Distance (d miles)	Frequency, f
$0 < d \leq 2$	9
$2 < d \leq 4$	8
$4 < d \leq 6$	6
$6 < d \leq 8$	4
$8 < d \leq 10$	3

a Calculate an estimate of the mean.

....

b Calculate an estimate of the standard deviation.

....

3 Here is some data.

32   21   25   18   17   30   22   19   27   24   31   41   26   24   17

Is 41 an outlier for this data? Explain your answer.

....

4 Simon and Alesha are judging a talent contest.
The table gives information about their rankings.

Contestant	Simon's rank	Alesha's rank
A	4	3
B	5	4
C	6	7
D	3	1
E	8	6
F	1	2
G	7	8
H	2	5

Calculate Spearman's coefficient of rank correlation for this data.

....

5 The table gives information about the marks obtained by a group of 12 students in a maths exam and in a physics exam.

Given $\Sigma xy = 49\,463$

$S_{xx} = 1357.7$

$S_{yy} = 1938.7$

Use $S_{xy} = \Sigma xy - \dfrac{\Sigma x \Sigma y}{n}$

Calculate the product-moment correlation coefficient for this data.
Give your answer correct to 2 decimal places.

Maths exam mark, x	Physics exam mark, y
63	68
48	55
72	67
75	72
67	78
49	55
55	42
81	86
64	70
68	48
50	72
74	51

6 The table gives information about the temperature, $t\,°C$ at different heights, $h\,$km, in the Earth's atmosphere.

You may use $S_{xy} = \Sigma xy - \dfrac{\Sigma x \Sigma y}{n}$

Calculate S_{th}

Height (h km)	Temperature ($t\,°C$)	
2	19	
3	16	
4	11	
5	0	
6	−7	
7	−19	
8	−24	

7 The mean score in a test is 64 marks and the standard deviation is 5.8 marks.
Alison scored 70 marks in the test.
Tim had a standardised score of 1.2 on the same test.
Who had the higher score? Explain your answer.

Needs more practice ▢ Almost there ▢ I'm proficient! ▢

AS LINKS
S1: 4.7 Comparing the distributions of data sets

4.1 Compare histograms and normal distributions

By the end of this section you will know how to:

* ✳ Compare histograms
* ✳ Compare normal distributions

Key points

✳ To compare histograms consider:
  - the modal class intervals for histograms with equal class intervals
  - the skew of the data
  - corresponding frequencies.

✳ To compare normal distributions consider:
  - the mean values
  - the standard deviations.

1 The speed of each serve in a tennis match was recorded.
Information about the results is shown in these histograms.

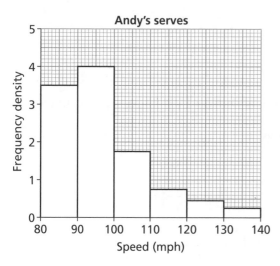

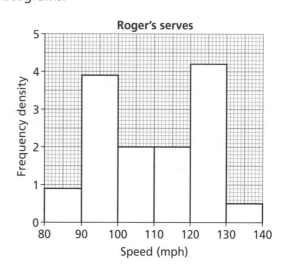

Compare the distributions of the speed of serve for the two players.
Write down three comparisons.

1 ....

> **Hint**
> Find the modal class interval for each player.

2 ....

> **Hint**
> Consider the symmetry or skew of the data.

3 ....

> **Hint**
> Compare the frequencies of very slow or very fast serves.

2 The weights of some female and some male Borzoi dogs were recorded.
Information about the results is shown in these histograms.

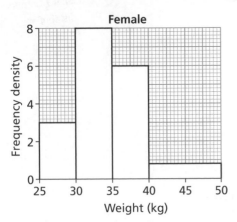

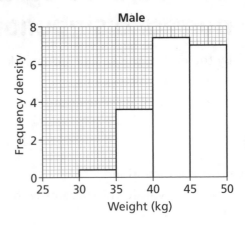

Compare the distributions of the weights of the Borzoi dogs.
Write down three comparisons.

1 ....

....

2 ....

....

3 ....

....

3 Students in Year 7 and in Year 11 were asked to record the amounts of time spent on homework
in one week.
Information about the results is shown in these histograms.

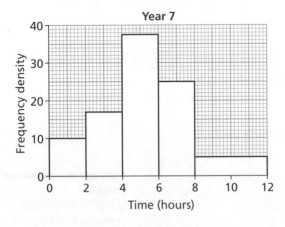

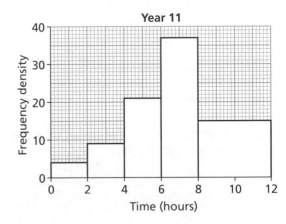

Compare the distributions of the time spent on homework.
Write down three comparisons.

1 ....

....

2 ....

....

3 ....

....

4 The normal distribution curves show the distributions of cholesterol levels for two groups of people. Group A represents people with normal levels of blood pressure and Group B represents people who have high blood pressure.

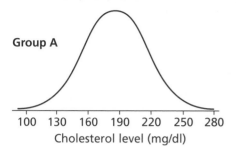

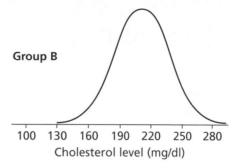

Describe two differences between the distributions for the two groups.

1 ....

....

....

> **Hint**
> Consider the mean values shown.

2 ....

....

....

> **Hint**
> Consider the standard deviations.

5 A machine cuts pieces of wood to a given length. The normal distribution curves show the distribution of lengths produced with the machine's initial setup and after some adjustment.

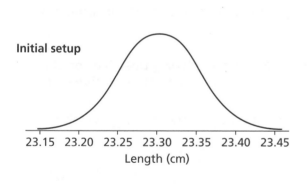

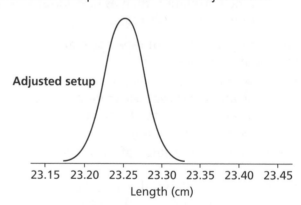

Describe two differences that result from making the adjustment.

1 ....

....

2 ....

....

AS LINKS

S1: Chapter 6 Correla

4.2 Identify and describe correlation in scatter graphs and interpret measures of correlation

By the end of this section you will know how to:
* Identify and describe correlation in scatter graphs
* Interpret measures of correlation

Key points

* Figure 1 shows **positive** correlation. Most points are in the 1st and 3rd quadrants.
* Figure 2 shows **negative** correlation. Most points are in the 2nd and 4th quadrants.
* Figure 3 shows **no** correlation. The points are spread over all four quadrants.

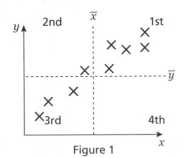
Figure 1

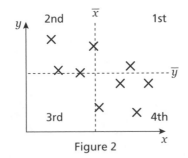
Figure 2

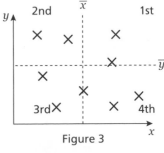
Figure 3

* With positive correlation, as one variable increases, the other variable increases.
* With negative correlation, as one variable increases, the other variable decreases.
* If there is no correlation then as one variable increases, the other variable will show no clear pattern of increase or decrease.

* Spearman's coefficient of rank correlation is denoted by r_s and the product-moment correlation coefficient is denoted by r.
* The value of r_s will always lie between -1 and $+1$:
  * $+1$ indicates a **perfect positive** correlation   • $r_s > 0.5$ indicates **strong positive** correlation
  * -1 indicates a **perfect negative** correlation   • $r_s < -0.5$ indicates **strong negative** correlation.
  * 0 indicates no correlation
* Interpretation of the value of r is the same as the interpretation of the value of r_s given above.

Guided

1   The scatter graph shows the heights, in metres, and the weights, in kg, of 10 athletes.

a   Describe the correlation shown by the scatter graph.

....

b   Given $S_{xx} = 0.01009$
          $S_{yy} = 94.376$
          $S_{xy} = 0.8368$

> **You should know**
> You need to know the formula for the PMCC. See Section 3.4.

Calculate the product-moment correlation coefficient for this data.
Give your answer correct to 2 decimal places.

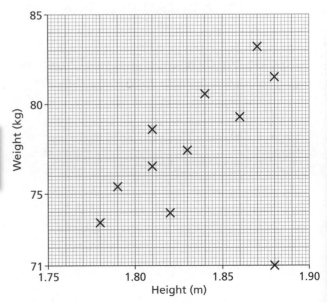

c Interpret your answer to part **b**.

....

....

2 The scatter graph gives information about the value of a particular make and model of car and its age.

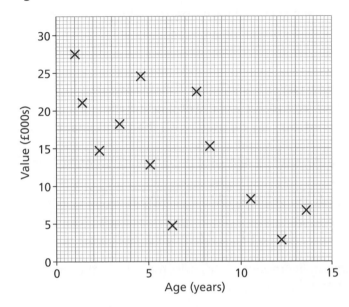

a Describe the correlation shown by the scatter graph.

....

The table shows the ranking of each car by value and by age.

Ranking by age, x	Ranking by value, y	d	d^2
12	1	11	121
11	4	7	49
10	7	3	9
9	5	4	16
8	2	6	36
7	8	−1	1
6	11	−5	25
5	3		
4	6		
3	9		
2	12		
1	10		

b Calculate Spearman's coefficient of rank correlation for this data.

....

c Interpret your answer to part **b**.

....

....

4.3 Identify trend and seasonality in time-series graphs

By the end of this section you will know how to:

* Use moving averages to draw a trend line
* Use the mean seasonal variation to make predictions

Key points

* Values of the **moving average** are plotted at the mid-points of the time intervals covered.
* The **trend line** is a line of best fit for the moving averages.
* The **mean seasonal variation** may be used, with the trend line, to make predictions.

Guided

1 The table shows the profit made by a large company each quarter from 2011 to 2012.

Year	2011				2012			
Quarter	1	2	3	4	1	2	3	4
Profit (£m)	23	29	47	41	27	35	55	49

a Plot the 4-point moving averages for this information on the time-series graph. The first two have been done for you.

Third point:

$$\frac{47 + 41 + 27 + 35}{4} = \text{.............................}$$

> **Hint**
> Plot this value at the mid-point of 3, 4, 1 and 2

Fourth point:

$$\frac{41 + 27 + 35 + \text{.........}}{4} = \text{.............................}$$

> **Hint**
> Plot this value at the mid-point of 4, 1, 2 and 3

Fifth point:

$$\frac{27 + 35 + \text{.........} + \text{.........}}{4} = \text{.............................}$$

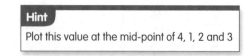

b Find an estimate of the mean seasonal variation for Quarter 1.

> **Hint**
> Draw a line of best fit for the moving averages.

> **Hint**
> Use the trend line to estimate the mean seasonal variation for Quarter 1.

....

c Predict the profit that will be made in Quarter 1 of 2013.

> **Hint**
> Predicted value = trend line value + mean seasonal variation for Quarter 1.

....

2 The table gives information about the number of people visiting a bird sanctuary each quarter from 2011 to 2012.

Year		2011				2012			
Quarter		1	2	3	4	1	2	3	4
Visitors (000s)		11	28	39	14	13	32	43	16
4-point moving average			23	23.5					

a Complete the table.

b Plot the 4-point moving averages and draw the trend line.

c Find an estimate of the mean seasonal variation in Quarter 2.

....

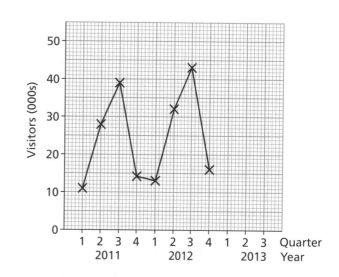

d A predicted value given for the number of visitors in Quarter 2 of 2013 is 30 000. Comment on the accuracy of this prediction.

....

....

3 The table shows how sales of rainwear in the UK varied over a two-year period.

Year	2011				2012			
Quarter	1	2	3	4	1	2	3	4
Sales (£m)	31	25	33	40	35	30	34	42

a Plot the 4-point moving averages for this information on the time-series graph.

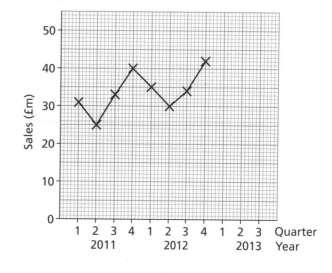

b Find an estimate of the mean seasonal variation for Quarter 1.

....

c Predict the sales figure for Quarter 1 in 2013. Comment on the reliability of your estimate.

....

....

Interpret and compare data

4.4

By the end of this section you will know how to:

✳ Interpret and compare data using a wide range of measures

Key points

✳ Interpreting and comparing data may involve using frequencies, totals, mean/median/mode/range, interquartile range, skew, standard deviation and standardised scores.

✳ The data to be compared may be presented in a variety of forms including diagrams and tables.

Guided

1 Greg organised a Fun Run in 2012 and in 2013.
Information about the times taken by the runners, in each year, is shown on the histograms.

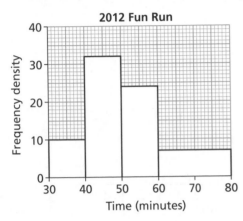
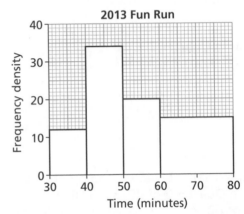

Compare the total numbers of runners taking part in the two events.

Hint

Multiply the width of a class interval by its height to obtain the frequency for that class interval.

Practice

2 48 students took two maths papers.
Information about the results is shown on the cumulative frequency graphs.

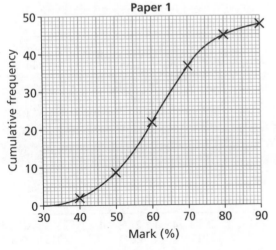
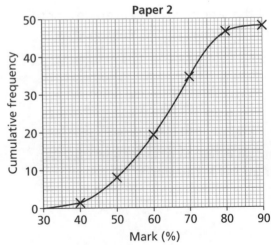

a Compare the medians of the marks on the two papers.

....

....

b Compare the interquartile ranges of the marks on the two papers.

....

....

c Compare the numbers of students on each paper who scored 60% or less.

....

....

3 A cricket match was played between teams from Stafford and from Sandon. Information about the numbers of runs scored is shown on the box plot diagrams.

a Compare the median scores.

....

....

b Compare the interquartile ranges.

....

....

c Describe the skew of each distribution.

....

....

....

> **You should know**
>
> If the median is closer to Q1 than to Q3 the skew is positive. If the median is closer to Q3 than to Q1 the skew is negative.

4 Tom checked the battery life of some laptop batteries after one year of use and after two years of use. Information about the battery life in each case is shown on the box plots.

Write down three comparisons.

1 ....

2 ....

3 ....

5 Nathan and Lisa took the same test in science.
The mean score for the test was 53 and the standard deviation was 7
Lisa's standardised score was 0.84
Nathan's test score was 61
Compare the performances of Nathan and Lisa.

$$\text{Standardised score} = \frac{(\text{Score} - \text{Mean})}{\text{Standard deviation}}$$

....

....

6 Philip took tests in maths and in biology. The table gives information about Philip's scores and the mean and standard deviation for each of the groups.

Subject	Philip's score	Mean score for group	Standard deviation for group
Maths	59	51	6
Biology	64	55	10

Compare Philip's performance in the two subjects.

....

....

7 In 1984 Carl Lewis won the 100 m Olympic final in a time of 9.99 seconds.
In 2012 Usain Bolt won the 100 m Olympic final in a time of 9.63 seconds.
The table gives some information about the recorded times of the finalists in each race.

Year	Mean	Standard deviation
1984	10.2375	0.105 682
2012	10.095	0.723 688

a Standardise the times for Carl Lewis and for Usain Bolt.

Lewis ....

Bolt ....

b Interpret the standardised scores.

....

....

One of the results for the 2012 final was an outlier. Asafa Powell suffered a groin injury and his time was 2 seconds behind the rest of the field.
If this result is discounted, the mean becomes 9.824 and the standard deviation becomes 0.110 694

c Use this information to calculate the new standardised time for Usain Bolt.

....

d State your conclusion.

....

....

Geometric means and chain base index numbers

By the end of this section you will know how to:
* Interpret and compare geometric means and chain base index numbers

Key points

* The **moving base index number** $= \dfrac{\text{Price in a given year}}{\text{Price in previous year}} \times 100$

* Over a period of years the moving base index numbers form a sequence called **chain base index numbers**.

* The **geometric mean** of a sequence of chain base index numbers gives a base index number which, if used in place of each of the chain base index numbers, would give the same end result.

* The geometric mean of some **fixed base** index numbers may also be found as an indication of a representative percentage change.

1 The table shows how the cost of raw materials for a factory changed between 2010 and 2013.

Year	2011	2012	2013
Percentage increase on previous year	5.2	3.8	7.5

a Complete the table to show the chain base index numbers.

Year	2011	2012	2013
Index number	…………	…………	…………

An increase of 5.2% gives a base index number of 100 + ………… = …………

b Find the geometric mean of the index numbers for 2011, 2012 and 2013.
Give your answer correct to 1 decimal place.

> **Hint**
> There are three index numbers, so find the cube root of their product.

…………………………………

c Interpret your answer to part **b**.

…………………………………………………………………………………………

…………………………………………………………………………………………

> **Hint**
> Describe your answer to part **b** as a percentage change.

2 Kevin has kept a record of the costs involved in heating his home. Information about these costs between 2008 and 2012 is shown in the table.

Year	2008	2009	2010	2011	2012
Cost (£)	421	489	536	587	620

a Complete the table to show the **chain** base index numbers.
Give each answer correct to 1 decimal place.

Year	2009	2010	2011	2012
Index number	…………	…………	…………	…………

For 2009: $\dfrac{489}{421} \times 100 =$ …………………………

For 2010: $\dfrac{536}{489} \times 100 =$ …………………………

b Find the geometric mean of the index numbers for
2009, 2010, 2011 and 2012.
Give your answer correct to 1 decimal place.

c Jill's heating costs have increased by an average of
11% per year over the same time period.
Compare this with the increase in Kevin's heating costs.

> **Hint**
> Use your answer to part **b** as a percentage
> increase to make the comparison.

3 The table gives information about the monthly rental cost of Tom's house in January 2010,
January 2011, January 2012 and January 2013.

Year	2010	2011	2012	2013
Rental cost (£)	576	615	642	710

a Complete the table to show the **chain** base index numbers.
Give each answer correct to 1 decimal place.

Year	2011	2012	2013
Index number	....	....	....

b Find the geometric mean of the index numbers for 2011, 2012 and 2013.
Give your answer correct to 1 decimal place.

c Suppose that the rental cost increased from £576 in January 2010 to £710 in January 2013 by the
same percentage each year. Find this percentage.

4 Bill has been monitoring the cost to buy a desktop computer of the same specification in January
each year from 2008 to 2013.

Year	2008	2009	2010	2011	2012	2013
Cost (£)	783	645	510	490	470	422

a Using 2008 as the base year, calculate index numbers for 2009, 2010, 2011, 2012 and 2013.
Give each answer correct to 1 decimal place.

Year	2009	2010	2011	2012	2013
Index number	....	....	....	....	....

b Find the geometric mean of the index numbers for 2009, 2010, 2011, 2012 and 2013.
Give your answer correct to 1 decimal place.

....

c Interpret your answer to part **b**.

....

....

Needs more practice ☐   Almost there ☐   I'm proficient! ☐

Interpreting diagrams

4.6

AS LINKS
S1: Chapter 4 Representation of data

By the end of this section you will know how to:

✳ Interpret back-to-back stem and leaf diagrams, box plots with outliers and Venn diagrams

✳ Interpret data from a variety of representations to solve a problem

Key points

✳ **Back-to-back stem and leaf** diagrams allow for direct comparisons to be made between two sets of data.

✳ Two or more **box plots** may be shown on the same scale to allow key features of the data to be compared directly.

✳ The minimum value indicated on a box plot is the smallest value not including any **outliers**. The maximum value indicated is the largest value not including any outliers.

✳ **Venn diagrams** may be used to represent information in such a way that related facts may be easier to deduce.

1 30 students took a test. The results for boys and for girls are shown separately on the back-to-back stem and leaf diagram.

Boys						Girls				
			6	3	4	8				
	9	7	3	2	5	3	4			
8	8	5	5	5	6	3	5	7	7	8
		9	8	4	7	4	6	7	9	
			7	8	1	3	3			

Key: 3 | 4 | 8 represents 43 marks for the boys and 48 marks for the girls.

a Compare the median mark for the boys with the median mark for the girls.

....

....

> **Hint**
> For 15 results, the position of the median is $(15 + 1) \div 2$

b Compare the interquartile range of the marks for the boys with the interquartile range of the marks for the girls.

....

....

> **Hint**
> The position of the lower quartile is $(15 + 1) \div 4$ and the position of the upper quartile is $3(15 + 1) \div 4$

Practice

2 The weights of some apples and some oranges, in grams, are shown in the back-to-back stem and leaf diagram.

	Apples					Oranges				
	7	5	4	2	14					
9	6	4	3	3	15	6				
		6	2	0	16	4	6			
			8	4	17	0	4	7	7	
				3	18	1	3	3	6	
					19	5	6	6	7	8
					20	0	1	6		

Key: 3 | 15 | 6 represents an apple of weight 153 grams and an orange of weight 156 grams.

Compare the median weight of the apples with the median weight of the oranges.

....

....

Step into AS

3 The back-to-back stem and leaf diagram gives information about the daily milk yields, in litres, of some Jersey cows and some Holstein cows.

	Holstein					Jersey					
8	8	6	5	1	5	6	7	7	7	9	
9	7	4	3	1	2	0	1	3	3	4	5	8
	7	6	4	3	3	0	2				
		1	0	4							

Key: 1 | 2 | 0 represents a Holstein cow with daily milk yield of 21 litres and a Jersey cow with daily milk yield of 20 litres.

Compare the milk yields for the Holstein cows and the Jersey cows.

....

....

Guided

4 Information about the times taken (in minutes) by some office workers to travel to work is shown on the box plot.

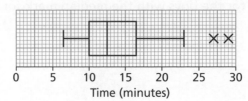

Time (minutes)

Hint
The outliers are represented as crosses on the diagram.

a Find the greatest time taken that is not an outlier.

.... minutes

b Find the greatest time taken overall.

.... minutes

5 The owner of a small company takes her employees
go-karting as part of a team-building exercise.
The three fastest lap times recorded, in seconds, were
61, 58 and 55.
Information about the lap times is shown on the partly
completed box plot diagram.

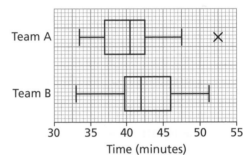

a Find the interquartile range of the lap times.

.... seconds

b Complete the diagram, indicating any outliers.

6 Two teams, A and B, competed against each other to
complete an orienteering course. Information about
the times taken is shown in the box plots.

a What was the winning time? .... minutes

b What was the slowest time? .... minutes

c Explain why the slowest time is an outlier.

....

....

....

....

....

7 Language students in a sixth form may study up to three languages. Information about the numbers
of students studying these languages is shown in the Venn diagram.

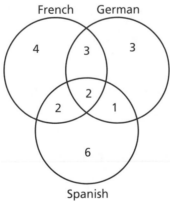

a How many students study only one language?

> **Hint**
>
> Four students study only French.
> Think about German and think
> about Spanish in the same way.

....

b How many students study two or more languages?

....

Practice

8 There are 53 books on Sarah's bookshelf.
25 books are about romance.
18 books are about comedy.
11 books are not about either romance or comedy.

   a Complete the Venn diagram to show this information.

   b How many of Sarah's books are about comedy but not romance?

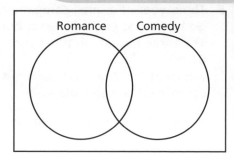

....

Don't forget!

✳ To compare histograms consider:
  - the modal class intervals of histograms with equal class intervals
  - the skew of the data
  - corresponding frequencies.

✳ To compare normal distributions consider:
  - the mean values
  - the standard deviations.

✳ For .... correlation, most points are in the 1st and 3rd quadrants.

✳ For .... correlation, most points are in the 2nd and 4th quadrants.

✳ The moving base index number $= \dfrac{\text{Price in a given year}}{\text{Price in .... year}} \times 100$

✳ Over a period of years the moving base index numbers form a sequence called .... base index numbers.

✳ The geometric mean of a sequence of chain base index numbers gives a base index number which, if used in place of each of the chain base index numbers, would give the .... end result.

✳ The geometric mean of some fixed base index numbers may also be found as an indication of a .... change.

✳ Back-to-back stem and leaf diagrams allow for direct .... to be made between two sets of data.

✳ Two or more box plots may be shown on the .... scale to allow key features of the data to be compared directly.

✳ The minimum value indicated on a box plot is the smallest value not including any .... The maximum value indicated is the largest value not including any ....

✳ Venn diagrams may be used to represent information in such a way that related .... may be easier to deduce.

Exam-style questions

1 The scatter graph gives information about the femur lengths and the heights of 10 students.

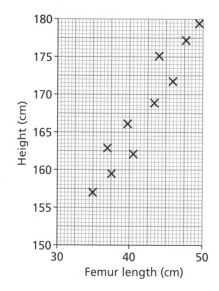

a Describe the correlation shown by the scatter graph.

....

....

b Given $S_{xx} = 204.7$ $S_{yy} = 547.0$ $S_{xy} = 315.4$

Calculate the product-moment correlation coefficient for this data. Give your answer correct to 2 decimal places.

....

c Interpret your answer to part **b**.

....

....

2 The table gives information about the number of maths revision books sold by a store in each quarter from 2011 to 2012

Year	2011				2012			
Quarter	1	2	3	4	1	2	3	4
Books sold	42	76	29	35	48	84	33	42

a Plot the 4-point moving averages for this information on the time-series graph.

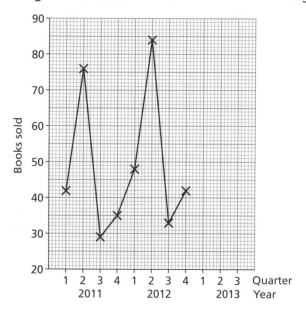

b Find an estimate of the mean seasonal variation for Quarter 1.

....

c Predict the number of books sold in Quarter 1 of 2013.

....

3 Ron has taken part in two triathlons.
The table gives some information,
about the times taken, in minutes.

Location	Ron's time	Mean (min)	Standard deviation
Buxton	79	92	10
Macclesfield	84	101	12

a Standardise Ron's time for each event.

Buxton ....

Macclesfield ....

b Compare Ron's performance in the two triathlons.

....

....

4 Each April, Ted buys some potted perennials to
plant in his garden. The table shows how much
Ted spent in 2010, 2011, 2012 and 2013.

Year	2010	2011	2012	2013
Cost (£)	96	124	106	135

a Take 2010 as the base year and complete the
table to show the base index numbers.
Give each answer correct to 1 decimal place.

Year	2011	2012	2013
Index number	....	....	....

b Find the geometric mean of the index numbers for 2011, 2012 and 2013.
Give your answer correct to 1 decimal place.

....

c Interpret your answer to part **b**.

....

....

5 The box plots give information about the daily numbers of visitors at a sea-life centre in August and
in September.

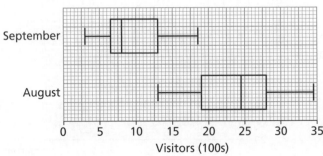

Visitors (100s)

a Make two comparisons.

1 ....

2 ....

b One day in September, there were 2800 visitors to the sea-life centre.
Show that this value is an outlier.

c Mark the position of the outlier on the diagram.

5.1 Probability and relative frequency

By the end of this section you will know how to:

* Use probability and relative frequency to estimate outcomes or make predictions

Key points

* In an experiment, the **relative frequency** of an event may be used to estimate the probability of the event.
* The relative frequency of an event is given by:

$$\frac{\text{Number of trials in which the event occurs}}{\text{Total number of trials}}$$

* Estimates of a probability are more reliable if the number of trials is large.
* The expected number of times that an event A will occur is given by $P(A) \times n$ where $P(A)$ is the probability that the event A will happen and n is the number of trials.
* Alternatively, the expected number of times that an event A will occur is given by the relative frequency of event $A \times n$ where n is the number of trials.

---

1 A spinner has three coloured sections. It can land on Red, on Green or on Yellow. The table shows the probabilities that a spinner will land on Red or on Green.

Colour	Red	Green	Yellow
Probability	0.35	0.28	....

> **Hint**
> Use the table to find the probability that the spinner lands on Yellow.

Carol spins the spinner 60 times.
Estimate the number of times that the spinner lands on Yellow.

....

2 Steven has a biased dice. He rolls the dice 85 times and obtains a score of 6 on 19 of these occasions.

   a Find the relative frequency of scoring a 6 with Steven's dice.
      Give your answer correct to 4 decimal places.

....

   b Steven is going to roll the dice a further 200 times.
      Estimate the number of these times that he will score a 6.

....

3 Ria has a coin that she thinks may be biased. She spins the coin 20 times and it lands on Heads 13 times.

    a Use this information to estimate the probability that the coin will land on Heads.

    ....

    b How can Ria find a more reliable estimate of the probability that the coin will land on Heads?

    ....

    ....

    ....

4 Sophie has a pack of cards in which half the cards are red (R) and half the cards are black (B). She is playing a game using the cards and a spinner. The spinner can land on red or black. The probability that it will land on red is 0.4

Sophie selects a card at random and spins the spinner.
She looks at the colour of the card and returns it to the pack.
Complete the tree diagram to show the probabilities.

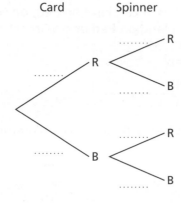

Card   Spinner

Sophie gets maximum points on her turn if she selects a black card and the spinner lands on black.

    a Find the probability that Sophie gets maximum points on her turn.

    ....

During the game, Sophie has 20 turns.

    b Estimate the number of times that Sophie gets maximum points during the game.

    ....

Sample space diagrams and Venn diagrams

AS LINKS
S1: 5.2 Solving probability problems by drawing Venn diagrams

By the end of this section you will know how to:

✳ Use sample space diagrams and Venn diagrams to calculate probabilities

Key points

✳ A **sample space diagram** shows the number of outcomes in a particular event and the total number of outcomes.

✳ The **number of outcomes in an event** and the **total number** of outcomes can be used to find the **probability** of the event.

✳ Information about outcomes can be found from a **Venn diagram** to find the probability of an event.

1 Two four-sided spinners are each numbered from 1 to 4.

Both spinners are spun and their scores are added together.

a Complete the sample space diagram.

		First spinner			
		1	**2**	**3**	**4**
	1	2	3		
Second spinner	**2**	3			
	3				
	4				

b Find the probability that the total score is less than 4.

> **Hint**
> Find the number of outcomes where the score is less than 4.

> **Hint**
> There are 16 outcomes altogether.

....

2 Three coins are spun. Find the probability that at least two of the coins land on Heads.

The possible outcomes are:

HHH

HHT

HTH

> **Hint**
> Continue the pattern to find all of the possible outcomes.

> **Hint**
> Identify the outcomes showing at least two Heads.

....

3 Matt has two ordinary dice. One of the dice is red and the other is blue.
In the sample space diagram:
- R indicates that the score on the red dice is higher than the score on the blue dice.
- B indicates that the score on the blue dice is higher than the score on the red dice.
- = indicates that the scores on the two dice are the same.

		Red dice					
		1	**2**	**3**	**4**	**5**	**6**
	1	=	R				
	2						
Blue	**3**					R	
dice	**4**		B				
	5						
	6				B		=

a Complete the sample space diagram.

b Find the probability that the score on the red dice is higher than the score on the blue dice.

....

c Find the probability that the score on the blue dice is at least as high as the score on the red dice.

> **Hint**
> This means that the score on the blue dice will be equal to, or greater than, the score on the red dice.

....

4 The Venn diagram gives information about the people who entered a talent contest.

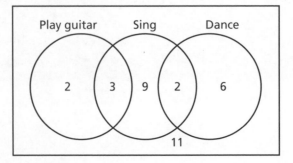

One person is selected at random.
Find the probability that this person sings but doesn't dance.

Number of people who sing but don't dance = 9 + ... = ...

Total number of people is 2 + 3 + ... = ...

P(Person selected sings but doesn't dance) = ...

5 A group of 14 students were discussing places that they had been to.
6 students had been to York.
9 students had been to Birmingham.
3 students had not been to either York or Birmingham.

   a Complete the Venn diagram.

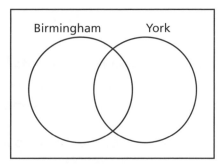

A student was selected at random.

   b Find the probability that this student had been to Birmingham and to York.

....

6 In a sixth form tutor group:
3 students studied maths and chemistry but not physics,
4 students studied physics and chemistry but not maths.

   a Complete the Venn diagram.

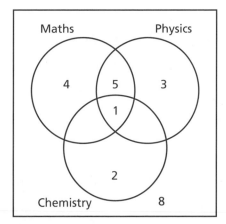

   b Find the probability that a student from this group, selected at random, studies maths and physics but not chemistry.

....

5.3

Tree diagrams

By the end of this section you will know how to:

✳ Multiply and add probabilities using tree diagrams

AS LINKS

S1: 5.5 Conditional probabilities on tree diagrams

Key points

✳ A tree diagram shows the **probabilities of combined events**.

✳ A **sequence of branches**, from one event to the next, represents a **sequence of outcomes**.

✳ To find the probability of a particular sequence of outcomes, **multiply the probabilities** on the corresponding branches.

✳ An event may be made from more than one sequence of outcomes. To find the probability of the event, **add the probabilities** of all of these sequences.

Guided

1 Stephanie throws a dice twice.
She is hoping for a 6 each time.

a Complete the tree diagram.

1st throw   2nd throw

$\frac{1}{6}$ 6

.... 6

$\frac{5}{6}$ Not 6

$\frac{5}{6}$ Not 6

.... 6

.... Not 6

> **You should know**
>
> The tree diagram is simplified by only considering whether the outcome is a 6 or not a 6 on each throw.

b Find the probability that Stephanie will get a 6 on both throws.

P(6 on both throws) = P(6 on 1st throw) × P(6 on 2nd throw)

> **Hint**
>
> The probabilities are the same for the second throw as they are for the first throw.

c Find the probability that Stephanie will get a 6 on one throw, but not on the other.

P(6 on one throw but not on the other)

= P(6 on 1st throw) × P(Not 6 on 2nd throw) + P(Not 6 on 1st throw) × ....

2 Paul has eight playing cards.
Five of the cards are red and three of the cards are black.
He selects a card at random and replaces it.
He then selects a second card at random.

a Complete the tree diagram to show this information.

1st card   2nd card

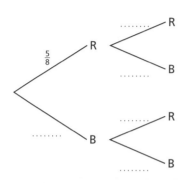

b Find the probability that Paul selects a red card followed by a black card.

....

c Find the probability that Paul selects two cards of the same colour.

....

3 Alice and Bob sell cars.
The probability that Alice hits her monthly sales target is 0.75
The probability that Bob hits his monthly sales target is 0.6

a Draw a probability tree diagram for this information.

b Work out the probability that at least one of Alice and Bob hits their monthly target.

....

Mutually exclusive events

AS LINKS
S1: 5.6 Mutually excl●
and independent eve●

5.4

By the end of this section you will know how to:
* Recognise mutually exclusive events
* Find P(A or B) where A and B are mutually exclusive events

Key points

* **Mutually exclusive events** are events that have no outcomes in common.
* If A and B are mutually exclusive events then:
  * A and B cannot both happen at the same time
  * **P(A or B) = P(A) + P(B)**
* **P(A or B)** may also be written as **P(A ∪ B)**

Guided

1   An ordinary dice is rolled.
   A is the event 'the score is even'.
   B is the event 'the score is 3'.
   Find P(A ∪ B)

   P(A) = ...

   P(B) = ...

   Events A and B have no common outcomes since .... is not an even score.

   A and B are .... events.

   P(A ∪ B) = P(A) + P(B) = ... + ... = ...

2   A and B are mutually exclusive events such that P(A) = 0.34 and P(B) = 0.25
   Find the probability that A or B will occur.

   Since A and B are mutually exclusive:

   P(A or B) = P(A) + P(B) = ...

3   In a swimming race:
   the probability that David wins is 0.16
   the probability that Paul wins is 0.24
   the probability that Shaun wins is 0.09

   Find the probability that David or Paul or Shaun wins the race.

> **Hint**
> There can only be one winner.

> **Hint**
> The rule for adding probabilities works for any number of mutually exclusive events.

....

Practice

4   Find P(A ∪ B) given that P(A) = $\frac{3}{8}$ and P(B) = $\frac{1}{3}$ where A and B are mutually exclusive events.

....

....

5 X and Y are events.
P(X) = 0.39
P(Y) = 0.52
P(X or Y) = 0.76

Show that X and Y are not mutually exclusive events.

6 Sharon picks a two-digit number X in some interval.

P(X is prime) = $\frac{3}{11}$

P(X is even) = $\frac{5}{11}$

a Find the probability that X is either even or prime.

b Find the probability that X is neither even nor prime.

Needs more practice ☐   Almost there ☐   I'm proficient! ☐

Combined events

AS LINKS

S1: 5.6 Mutually exclusive and independent events

5.5

By the end of this section you will know how to:

✳ Recognise independent events

✳ Find P($A \cap B$) where A and B are independent events

✳ Find P($A \cup B$) where A and B are any events

Key points

✳ Two events are said to be **independent** if the outcome of one does not affect the outcome of the other.

✳ If A and B are **independent** events then **P(A and B) = P(A) × P(B)**

✳ **P(A and B)** may also be written as **P($A \cap B$)**

✳ The rule applies to **any number** of independent events.

✳ If A, B and C are **independent** events then **P($A \cap B \cap C$) = P(A) × P(B) × P(C)**

✳ P(A or B) represents the probability that A or B **or both** will happen.

✳ **P(A or B)** may be written as **P($A \cup B$)**

✳ For any **two events** A and B, **P($A \cup B$) = P(A) + P(B) − P($A \cap B$)**

✳ In the **special case** where A and B are **mutually exclusive**, **P($A \cap B$) = 0** and the rule simplifies to **P($A \cup B$) = P(A) + P(B)**

Guided

1 Kim spins a coin twice.
Find the probability that the coin will land on Heads on the first spin **and** it will land on Heads on the second spin.

$P(HH) = P(H) \times P(H) = \text{.........} \times \text{.........} = \text{.........................}$

2 Jack spins a coin three times.
What is the probability that he gets Tails all three times?

$P(TTT) = P(T) \times \text{.........} \times \text{.........} = \text{.........} \times \text{.........} \times \text{.........} = \text{.........................}$

Practice

3 Amy has a spinner that can land on blue (B) or on red (R).
$P(B) = \frac{3}{5} \qquad P(R) = \frac{2}{5}$

Amy spins the spinner three times.
Find the probability that the spinner lands on red **and** then it lands on blue **and** then it lands on red again.

4 X and Y are two events.
$P(X) = \frac{2}{3} \qquad P(Y) = \frac{3}{4} \qquad P(X \cap Y) = \frac{5}{12}$
Show that X and Y are not independent events.

Step into AS

5 A bag contains four yellow counters and three green counters.
Josh selects a counter at random and replaces it.
Josh then selects a second counter at random.

Find the probability that both counters are yellow.

Guided

6 X and Y are independent events.
$P(X) = 0.3 \qquad P(Y) = 0.6$
Find $P(X \cup Y)$

$P(X \cup Y) = P(X) + P(Y) - P(X \cap Y)$

7 A ten-sided spinner has seven orange sections and three purple sections.
Four of the orange sections are labelled with an odd number.
One of the purple sections is labelled with an odd number.

Katie spins the spinner in a game. She will score a point if the spinner
lands on a purple section or if it lands on an odd number.

Find the probability that Katie scores a point on her next spin.

Let A be the event that the spinner lands on a purple section.

Let B be the event that the spinner lands on an odd-numbered section.

$P(A) = $ .... $\qquad P(B) = $ ....

$P(A \cap B) = $ ....

$P(A \cup B) = P(A) + P(B) - P(A \cap B)$

$P(A \cup B) = $ .... $+$ .... $-$ ....

$\qquad = $ ....

Hint

It's easy to get confused but the rules are there to help.

Hint

Define the events and use the relevant formula.

Hint

$A \cap B$ is represented by the sections that are coloured purple **and** are labelled with an odd number.

8 The probability that James passes his maths exam is 0.7
The probability that he passes his statistics exam is 0.8
The probability that he passes both exams is 0.6

James will get onto the course he wants to study if he passes either exam.

Find the probability that James will get onto the course.

....

9 Jen has a red dice and a blue dice. Both dice are biased.
The probability that the red dice will land on 6 is 0.3
The probability that the blue dice will land on 6 is 0.25

Jen rolls both dice.
Work out the probability that at least one of the dice lands on 6.

....

Conditional probabilities

5.6

AS LINKS

S1: 5.4 Solving proble
using conditional
probability

By the end of this section you will know how to:
* Recognise and calculate conditional probabilities

Key points

* Read **P(B|A)** as **'the probability of B given A'** which means the probability that B will happen given that A has already happened.

* In the case where A and B are **independent**, **P(B|A) = P(B)**

* If the outcome of B is influenced by the outcome of A then **P(B|A) ≠ P(B)**

* **P(A ∩ B) = P(A) × P(B|A)**

* It follows that $P(B|A) = \dfrac{P(A \cap B)}{P(A)}$

Guided

1 A bag contains six yellow counters and four green counters.
Tim takes out one counter at random.
He then takes a second counter out at random without replacing the first one.

> **You should know**
>
> This is another important situation to be familiar with called **without replacement**.

a Find the probability that both counters are green.

> **Hint**
>
> There are nine counters left once the first has been removed.

$$P(GG) = \frac{4}{\dots} \times \frac{3}{\dots} = \dots$$

> **Hint**
>
> If the first counter taken out is green then there will only be three green counters to choose from when the second counter is selected.

b Find the probability that only one of the counters taken out is green.

> **Hint**
>
> This situation may be represented on a tree diagram.

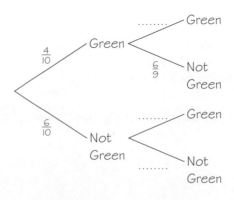

First counter   Second counter

P(only one green) = P(1st green and 2nd not green) + P(1st not green and 2nd green)

$$= \frac{4}{10} \times \frac{6}{9} + \dots \times \dots$$

$$= \dots$$

2 The probability that it will rain on Wednesday is 0.5
If it rains on Wednesday, the probability that it will rain on Thursday is 0.6
If it doesn't rain on Wednesday, the probability that it will rain on Thursday is 0.4

  a Find the probability that it will rain on Wednesday and on Thursday.

  b Find the probability that it will rain on Wednesday or on Thursday but not on both days.

3 A card is selected at random from a pack of 52 playing cards.
Given that the card is a spade, find the probability that
it is a queen.

Let A be the event that the card is a spade.

Let B be the event that the card is a queen.

$P(A \cap B) = $ ....

$P(A) = $ ....

$P(B|A) = \dfrac{P(A \cap B)}{P(A)}$

> **Hint**
> The words 'given that' tell you that this is conditional probability.

> **Hint**
> To use the formula, choose A to be the event that is 'given'.

> **Hint**
> $P(A \cap B)$ is the probability that the card is a spade **and** a queen i.e. it is the Queen of Spades.

4 Karen and Steve are photographers at a wedding. They each take photographs during the day and in the evening. Information about the numbers of photographs that they took is given in the table.

Photographer	Day	Evening
Karen	120	50
Steve	90	60

A photograph is selected at random.

a Find the probability that the photograph was taken in the evening.

....

b Find the probability that Karen took the photograph, given that it was taken in the evening.

....

5 In a survey, people were asked about the television programmes that they like to watch. Information about the results is shown on the Venn diagram.

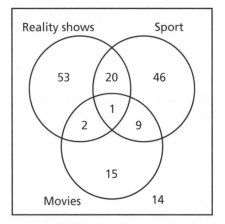

One person who completed the survey is selected at random.

a Find the probability that this person likes to watch sport and movies.

....

b Given that the person selected likes sport, work out the probability that they like movies.

....

Binomial probabilities

5.7

By the end of this section you will know how to:
* Identify and calculate binomial probabilities

Key points

* You can use the results for **binomial** probabilities when:
  * there is a **fixed number** of trials
  * the probability of success is the **same** for each trial
  * the trials are **independent**.
* If there are r successes out of n trials then there are different **combinations** of ways in which those successes occur. The number of combinations is given by $^nC_r = \dfrac{n!}{r!(n-r)!}$ Your calculator may have a special key to calculate this.
* The probability that there are r successes out of n trials is $^nC_r p^r(1-p)^{n-r}$ where p is the probability of success for each trial.

1   Jason has a biased coin.
    The probability that the coin lands on Heads is 0.43
    Jason spins the coin six times.

   a   Work out the probability that the coin lands on Heads twice.
       Give your answer correct to 3 decimal places.

       $n = $ ....

       $p = 0.43$ so $1 - p = $ ....

       $r = $ ....

       P(two Heads) $= {}^6C_2 \times 0.43^2 \times$ ....$^4 = $ ....

                                    $= $ .... (3 d.p.)

   > **Hint**
   > Start by finding the values of n, p and r.

   > **Hint**
   > In this case, a 'success' is when the coin lands on Heads.

   b   Find the probability that the coin lands on Heads at least once.
       Give your answer correct to 3 decimal places.

       P(0 Heads) $=$ P(six Tails) $= 0.57$·········· $= $ ....

       P(at least one Head) $= $ ....

                            $= $ .... (3 d.p.)

   > **Hint**
   > At least one Head means one or more Heads.
   > The sum of all the probabilities $= 1$,
   > so P(at least one Head) $= 1 -$ P(0 Heads).

2 The probability that a newborn child is a boy is 0.5

In a maternity hospital, eight children are born on one day.

   a Find the probability that there are three boys and five girls.
     Give your answer correct to 3 decimal places.

....

   b Find the probability that at least one of the children is a boy.
     Give your answer correct to 3 decimal places.

....

3 In a multiple choice test there are four options for each question and there are ten questions.

Nathan guesses all of the answers.

   a Find the probability that Nathan gives exactly three correct answers.

....

   b Find the probability that Nathan gives at least one correct answer.

....

The normal distribution

5.8

By the end of this section you will know how to:

* Find probabilities using standard normal distribution tables

AS LINKS

S1: Chapter 9 The normal distribution

Key points

* A random variable X with mean value μ and standard deviation σ may be standardised using
  $$Z = \frac{X - \mu}{\sigma}$$

* Standardised values may then be used with standard normal distribution tables to **calculate probabilities**.

* Standard normal distribution tables show $P(Z < z) = \Phi(z)$ for $z > 0$.

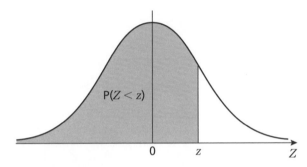

* Using the symmetry of the normal distribution:
  * $P(Z > z) = 1 - P(Z < z) = 1 - \Phi(z)$
  * $\Phi(-z) = 1 - \Phi(z)$

1 The random variable X is normally distributed with mean 50 and standard deviation 12.

a Find $P(X < 55)$

$$P(X < 55) = P\left(Z < \frac{55 - \text{........}}{12}\right) = P(Z < \text{........})$$

$$= \Phi(\text{........})$$

$$= \text{........................}$$

> **Hint**
>
> First rewrite the condition in terms of the standard variable Z.

> **Hint**
>
> Now use the standard normal distribution table on page 83 to look up the probability.

b Find $P(X > 70)$

$$P(X > 70) = P\left(Z > \frac{\text{........} - \text{........}}{12}\right) = P(Z > \text{........})$$

$$= 1 - P(Z < \text{........})$$

$$= 1 - \Phi(\text{........})$$

$$= \text{........................}$$

> **Hint**
>
> As before, first rewrite the condition in terms of the standard variable Z.

> **Hint**
>
> Rewrite again using $P(Z < \text{........})$ so that the table on page 83 can be used.

c Find $P(X < 35)$

$$P(X < 35) = P\left(Z < \frac{\text{........} - \text{........}}{\text{........}}\right) = P(Z < -1.25)$$

$$= \Phi(-1.25)$$

$$= \text{........................}$$

$$= \text{........................}$$

> **Hint**
>
> Use $\Phi(-z) = 1 - \Phi(z)$

2 The random variable X is normally distributed with mean 68 and standard deviation 15.

a Find $P(X < 100)$

....

b Find $P(X > 80)$

....

c Find $P(X < 50)$

....

3 The marks of a group of students in an examination may be modelled by a normal distribution with mean 58 and standard deviation 7.

A student is picked at random.

a Find the probability that this student scored less than 45 marks.

....

b 76% of students pass the exam. Calculate the pass mark.

Hint

Use the table on page 83 to find the value of z such that $\Phi(z) = 0.76$

....

Don't forget!

✳ The expected number of times that an event A will occur is given by .... where P(A) is the probability that the event A will happen and n is the number of trials.

✳ A sample space diagram shows the number of outcomes in a particular .... and the total number of outcomes.

✳ To find the probability of a particular sequence of outcomes, using a tree diagram, ... the probabilities on the corresponding branches.

✳ An event may be made from more than one sequence of outcomes. To find the probability of the event, ... the probabilities of all of these sequences.

✳ Mutually exclusive events are events that have no .... in common.

✳ If A and B are mutually exclusive events then:

• A and B cannot both .... at the same time

• P(A or B) = ...

✳ P(A or B) may also be written as ....

✳ Two events are said to be independent if the outcome of one .... the other.

✳ If A and B are independent events then P(A and B) = ...

✳ P(A and B) may also be written as ....

✳ P(A or B) represents the probability that A or B or .... will happen.

✳ For any two events A and B, P($A \cup B$) = ...

✳ In the special case where A and B are mutually exclusive, P($A \cap B$) = ... and the rule simplifies to P($A \cup B$) = ...

✳ P($A \cap B$) = ... $\times$ P($B|A$)

✳ It follows that P($B|A$) = $\dfrac{.........................}{.........................}$

✳ You can use the results for binomial probabilities when:

• there is a .... number of trials

• the probability of success is the ....

• the trials are ....

✳ If there are r successes out of n trials then there are different combinations of ways in which those successes occur. The number of combinations is given by $^nCr = \dfrac{.............................}{.............................}$

✱ The probability that there are r successes out of n trials is ....
where p is the probability of success for each trial.

✱ A random variable X with mean value μ and standard deviation σ may be standardised using

$$Z = \frac{\text{................}}{\text{................}}$$

✱ From the tables, ... $= \Phi(z)$

✱ $P(Z > z) = 1 - P$.................... $= 1 -$ ....

✱ $\Phi(-z) =$ ....

Exam-style questions

1 There are 48 people on a beach.
22 of the people have a parasol.
29 of the people are wearing sunglasses.
11 people do not have a parasol and are not wearing sunglasses.

a Complete the Venn diagram to show this information.

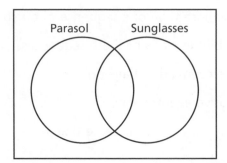

One of the people is selected at random.

b Given that this person has a parasol, find the probability that they are also wearing sunglasses.

....

2 Mark has a spinner.
The probability that the spinner lands on red is 0.7
The probability that the spinner lands on blue is 0.3

Mark spins the spinner twice.
Find the probability that the spinner lands on the same colour both times.

....

3 Rob is going to take his driving test.
He must pass both the theory part and the practical part to pass the test.
The probability that he fails the theory part is 0.1
The probability that he fails the practical part is 0.2
The results for the two parts are independent.
Find the probability that Rob passes the test.

....

4 G and H are independent events.

$P(G) = 0.34$
$P(H) = 0.2$

a Find $P(G \cup H)$

....

X and Y are two events.

$P(X) = 0.3$
$P(Y) = 0.5$
$P(X|Y) = 0.45$

b Find $P(Y|X)$

....

5 A bag contains three red crayons and five blue crayons.
Sasha takes, at random, two of the crayons without replacement.

   a Complete the tree diagram to show this information.

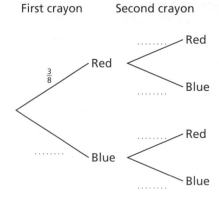

First crayon   Second crayon

$\frac{3}{8}$

   b Work out the probability that one of the crayons is red and the other crayon is blue.

....

6 Sara has three green cards and two pink cards.
She takes one card at random and replaces it.
She does this seven times.

   a Find the probability that of the seven cards she takes, four of them will be pink.

....

   b Find the probability that at least one of the selected cards is pink.

....

7 A random variable X is normally distributed with mean value 29.5 and standard deviation 4.6

   a Write down the median of the distribution.

....

   b Find $P(X < 35)$

....

   c Find $P(X > 25)$

....

Practice Paper

Time: 2 hours

Edexcel publishes Sample Assessment Material on its website. This Practice Exam Paper has been written to help you practise what you have learned and may not be representative of a real exam paper.

1 The headteacher of a school wants to find out what the students think about the proposed changes to the school uniform.

   a Describe a sampling frame that the headteacher could use.

   A list

   (1)

   b Write down one advantage of taking a sample.

   Takes less time

   (1)

   (Total for Question 1 is 2 marks)

2 Leanne phoned a number of insurance companies to find out about the cost of insuring her car. The table shows a summary of this information.

Lowest price	£420
Lower quartile	£465
Median	£495
Upper quartile	£525
Highest price	£648

IQr = 60

   a Show that £648 is an outlier for this distribution.

   465 ✗ 1.5 × 60 = 375

   525 + 1.5 × 60 = 615

   648 > 615

   (3)

   £648 is the only outlier and the highest price that is not an outlier is £610.

   b On the grid, draw a box plot for Leanne's insurance quotes.

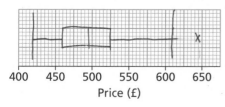

   (3)

   (Total for Question 2 is 6 marks)

3 A group of students were given a test on completion of a statistics course.
The group were then given some revision lessons before being tested again.

Marks in the first test

48	43	56	51	76	78	64	63	45	68
55	72	70	64	58	55	49	68	75	66
50	42	66	51	78	63	68	53	47	72

Marks in the second test

68	47	53	76	66	48	67	72	78	80
55	72	67	50	74	65	71	75	67	63
56	67	69	61	77	72	59	67	83	64

a Draw an ordered back-to-back stem and leaf diagram for this information.
You must show a key.

First test		**Second test**
	4	
	5	
	6	
	7	
	8	

(2)

b Compare the distribution of results in the two tests.

1 ....

2 ....

(2)

(Total for Question 3 is 4 marks)

---

4 Jimmy is going to play in two football matches.
The probability that he will score in the first match is 0.4
If he scores in the first match then the probability that he will score in the second match is 0.6
If he doesn't score in the first match then the probability that he will score in the second match is 0.3

a Complete the tree diagram for this information.

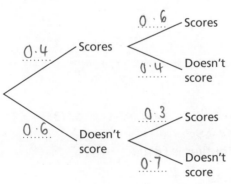

First match   Second match

0.4 — Scores
0.6 — Scores
0.4 — Doesn't score
0.6 — Doesn't score
0.3 — Scores
0.7 — Doesn't score

(3)

b Work out the probability that Jimmy scores in one match but not in the other.

0·4 × 0·4 = 0·16
0·6 × 0·3 ~ 0·18   = 0·34

.... 0·34 ....

(2)

(Total for Question 4 is 5 marks)

5 A and B are independent events.
$P(A) = 0.16$
$P(B) = 0.25$

a Find $P(A \cap B)$

$0.16 \times 0.25 = 0.04$

0.04

(1)

b Find $P(A \cup B)$

$P(A \cup B) = P(A) + P(B) - P(A+B)$
$= P(0.16) + P(0.25) - 0.04$
$= 0.37$

0.37

(2)

X and Y are two events.
$P(X) = 0.7$
$P(Y) = 0.2$
$P(X|Y) = 0.8$

c Find $P(X \cap Y)$

$0.8 \times 0.2 = 0.16$

0.16

(1)

d Find $P(Y|X)$

$\dfrac{0.16}{0.7} = 0.228$

0.228

(1)

(Total for Question 5 is 5 marks)

---

6 Gabriel asked 30 students how many newspapers they read last week.
The table shows his results.

Number of newspapers (x)	Frequency (f)	fx
0	4	0
1	2	2
2	1	2
3	3	9
4	2	8
5	10	50
6	6	36
7	2	14

121

Calculate the standard deviation for the number of newspapers read.
Give your answer to 2 decimal places.
You may use $\Sigma fx^2 = 629$

$$\sqrt{\frac{\Sigma fx^2}{\Sigma f} - \left(\frac{\Sigma fx}{\Sigma f}\right)^2} = \sqrt{\frac{629}{30} - \left(\frac{121}{30}\right)^2} = 2.167$$

$= 2.17$

(Total for Question 6 is 3 marks)

7 In a survey of 25 musicians, it was found that 8 play the guitar, 19 play the piano and 3 sing but do not play a musical instrument.

a Complete the Venn diagram to show this information.

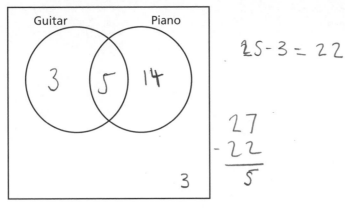

$25 - 3 = 22$

$\begin{array}{r} 27 \\ -22 \\ \hline 5 \end{array}$

(2)

b One of these musicians is picked at random.
Given that this musician plays the piano, find the probability that this musician also plays the guitar.

$6 + ? =$

$5/25$

(2)

(Total for Question 7 is 4 marks)

---

8 Larry bought a new car of the same type every year from 2009 to 2013.
The table shows how much the cars cost.

Year	2009	2010	2011	2012	2013
Cost	£17 800	£18 500	£19 700	£21 300	£24 600

a Take 2009 as the base year and calculate the index numbers for 2011, 2012 and 2013 and complete the table.
Give each answer correct to 1 decimal place.

Year	2010	2011	2012	2013
Index number	103.9	110.7	119.7	138.2

(3)

b Calculate the geometric mean of the index numbers in the table.
Give your answer correct to 1 decimal place.

$$\sqrt[4]{103.9 \times 110.7 \times 119.7 \times 138.2} = 117.4$$

117.4

(1)

c Interpret your answer to part **b**.

There is an average increase of 17.4%.

(2)

(Total for Question 8 is 6 marks)

9 The table gives information about the times taken by a group of runners to complete a cross-country course.

Time (*t* minutes)	Number of runners	fd
$20 < t \leqslant 22$	6	3
$22 < t \leqslant 24$	8	4
$24 < t \leqslant 28$	22	5.5
$28 < t \leqslant 34$	15	2.5
$34 < t \leqslant 40$	12	2

a Draw a histogram for this information.

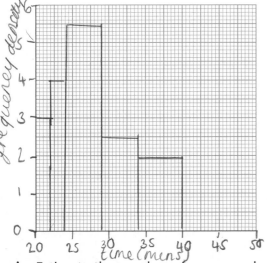

(3)

b Estimate the number of runners who took 30 minutes or less to complete the course.

$6 + 8 + 22 + 5 = 41$

41
....

(2)

(Total for Question 9 is 5 marks)

---

10 The table gives information about the numbers of Tae Kwon Do students at a club and their grades.

	Belt colour					
	White	Yellow	Green	Blue	Red	Total
Male	4	5	8	6	3	26
Female	3	4	9	5	3	24
Total	7	9	17	11	6	50

Mark is going to take a sample of 20 of these students stratified by belt colour and by gender. Work out the number of female blue belt students in his sample.

$\dfrac{5}{50} \times 20 = 2$

2
....

(Total for Question 10 is 2 marks)

11 In a television talent show, each act is given a score by a panel of judges.
The public then vote for their favourite act by telephone.
The table shows the acts ranked in order by the scores of the judges.

Act	Rank of scores	% of votes received	d	d^2
A	1	19 6	−5	25
B	2	28 8	−6	36
C	3	21 7	−4	16
D	4	10 5	−1	1
E	5	6 2 3		9
F	6	8 4 2		4
G	7	7 3 4		16
H	8	1 1 7		49

156

a Calculate Spearman's coefficient of rank correlation for this information.

$$1 - \frac{6 \times 156}{8(8^2-1)} = -0.857$$

$$= 0.857$$

0.857

(3)

b Interpret your answer in terms of the correlation between the scores given by the judges and the percentage of the public vote received.
Give a reason for your answer.

Strong positive correlation (over 0.5)

(1)

(Total for Question 11 is 4 marks)

---

12 A landowner wants to estimate the number of squirrels in a forest. A sample of 60 squirrels is captured and tagged. The squirrels are then released back into the forest. A second sample of 48 squirrels is then found to contain 8 squirrels that were tagged in the first sample.

a Use the information to work out an estimate of the number of squirrels in the forest.

$$\frac{60 \times 48}{8} = 360$$

(2)

b State two things that the landowner should have done in order to obtain a reliable estimate.

1 ....

2 ....

(2)

(Total for Question 12 is 4 marks)

13 The table gives information about the numbers of geometry sets sold by a store in each quarter from 2011 to 2012.

Year	2011				2012			
Quarter	1	2	3	4	1	2	3	4
Sets sold	26	68	80	22	26	72	88	26
4-point moving average			49	49	50	52	53	

a Complete the table.

(3)

b Plot the 4-point moving averages for this information on the time-series graph.

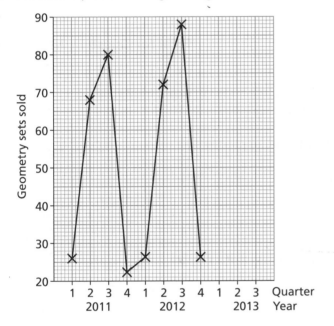

(1)

c Find an estimate of the mean seasonal variation for Quarter 1.

26
....

(2)

d Predict the number of geometry sets sold for Quarter 1 in 2013.

....

(2)

(Total for Question 13 is 8 marks)

14 An examiner has 200 exam papers to mark.
The box plots show information about the times she takes to mark the papers.

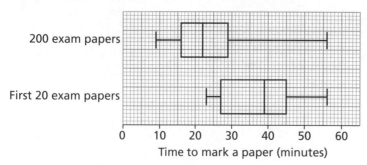

200 exam papers

First 20 exam papers

0   10   20   30   40   50   60
Time to mark a paper (minutes)

Compare the distributions of the times for the first 20 papers with the times for all 200 papers.
Write down three comparisons.

1 Median lower for 200 exam papers

2 Range bigger for 200 exam papers

3 1aR bigger for first 20 exam papers

(Total for Question 14 is 3 marks)

15 Some A level students took an exam in Statistics and some took an exam in Mechanics.
The table gives some information about their scores.

Exam	Mean	Standard deviation
Statistics	65	7
Mechanics	56	8

Alice scored 68 marks in Statistics.
Bob scored 62 marks in Mechanics.

a Calculate the standardised scores for Alice and Bob.

$$\frac{68-65}{7} = 0.428571$$

$$\frac{62-56}{8} = 0.75$$

Alice's standardised score 0.428571

Bob's standardised score 0.75

(4)

b Interpret the standardised scores.

Bob did better than Alice

(1)

(Total for Question 15 is 5 marks)

16 A cake shop sells apple pies from two different suppliers.
The normal distribution curves show the distribution of weights of the pies from each supplier.

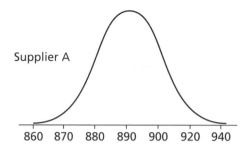

Supplier A

860 870 880 890 900 920 940

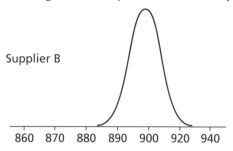

Supplier B

860 870 880 890 900 920 940

Describe two differences in the weight distributions of the pies.

1 .....Supplier B has a higher mean...

2 .....Supplier A has a bigger range...

(Total for Question 16 is 2 marks)

17 There are 8 counters in a bag. 5 of the counters are each labelled with an odd number.
The other 3 counters are each labelled with an even number.
James takes 2 counters at random from the bag without replacement.
He adds the numbers shown on the counters. Work out the probability that the total is even.

odd + odd = even
even + even = even

$5/8 \times 4/7 = 5/14$
$3/8 \times 2/7 = 3/28$ ⎤ = 13/28

13/28
....

(Total for Question 17 is 4 marks)

18 A continuous random variable, X, is normally distributed with mean 45 and standard deviation 10.
Using standard normal distribution tables, find the probability that:

a $X < 62$

$= 1.7$

0.9554
....
(2)

b $X > 39$ $\dfrac{39 - 45}{10} = -0.6$

0.7257
....
(2)

c $25 < X < 34$

0.1129
....
(2)

(Total for Question 18 is 6 marks)

19 The table gives information about the average January temperature, x °C, and the latitude, y °N, of 10 North American cities.

Temperature (x °C)	Latitude (y °N)	xy
28	8	224
24	22	528
17	32	544
14	36	504
12	41	492
10	46	460
−1	52	−52
4	56	224
2	60	120
−4	66	−264

2780

a Calculate S_{xy} for the data in the table.

You may use $S_{xy} = \Sigma xy - \dfrac{\Sigma x \Sigma y}{n}$

$$2780 - \frac{106 \times 419}{10} = -1661.4$$

.... −1661.4

(3)

b Calculate the product-moment correlation coefficient for the data.
You may use $S_{xx} = 1002.4$ and $S_{yy} = 2904.9$

$r = \dfrac{S_{xy}}{\sqrt{S_{xx} \times S_{yy}}}$

$r = \dfrac{-1661.4}{\sqrt{1002.4 \times 2904.9}} = -0.9736$

.... −0.9736

(3)

(Total for Question 19 is 6 marks)

---

20 A student in a class rolls an ordinary dice five times and counts the number of times the dice lands on six.

a Find the probability that no sixes will be scored in five throws.

....

(2)

b Find the probability that at least two sixes will be scored in five throws.

....

(2)

c There are 30 students in the class. Estimate the number of students who will score at least two sixes.

....

(2)

(Total for Question 20 is 6 marks)

TOTAL FOR PAPER IS 90 MARKS

Appendix

The normal distribution function

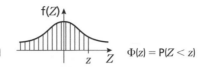

$\Phi(z) = P(Z < z)$

z	P(Z < z)	z	P(Z < z)	z	P(Z < z)	z	P(Z < z)	z	P(Z < z)
0.00	0.5000	0.50	0.6915	1.00	0.8413	1.50	0.9332	2.00	0.9772
0.01	0.5040	0.51	0.6950	1.01	0.8438	1.51	0.9345	2.02	0.9783
0.02	0.5080	0.52	0.6985	1.02	0.8461	1.52	0.9357	2.04	0.9793
0.03	0.5120	0.53	0.7019	1.03	0.8485	1.53	0.9370	2.06	0.9803
0.04	0.5160	0.54	0.7054	1.04	0.8508	1.54	0.9382	2.08	0.9812
0.05	0.5199	0.55	0.7088	1.05	0.8531	1.55	0.9394	2.10	0.9821
0.06	0.5239	0.56	0.7123	1.06	0.8554	1.56	0.9406	2.12	0.9830
0.07	0.5279	0.57	0.7157	1.07	0.8577	1.57	0.9418	2.14	0.9838
0.08	0.5319	0.58	0.7190	1.08	0.8599	1.58	0.9429	2.16	0.9846
0.09	0.5359	0.59	0.7224	1.09	0.8621	1.59	0.9441	2.18	0.9854
0.10	0.5398	0.60	0.7257	1.10	0.8643	1.60	0.9452	2.20	0.9861
0.11	0.5438	0.61	0.7291	1.11	0.8665	1.61	0.9463	2.22	0.9868
0.12	0.5478	0.62	0.7324	1.12	0.8686	1.62	0.9474	2.24	0.9875
0.13	0.5517	0.63	0.7357	1.13	0.8708	1.63	0.9484	2.26	0.9881
0.14	0.5557	0.64	0.7389	1.14	0.8729	1.64	0.9495	2.28	0.9887
0.15	0.5596	0.65	0.7422	1.15	0.8749	1.65	0.9505	2.30	0.9893
0.16	0.5636	0.66	0.7454	1.16	0.8770	1.66	0.9515	2.32	0.9898
0.17	0.5675	0.67	0.7486	1.17	0.8790	1.67	0.9525	2.34	0.9904
0.18	0.5714	0.68	0.7517	1.18	0.8810	1.68	0.9535	2.36	0.9909
0.19	0.5753	0.69	0.7549	1.19	0.8830	1.69	0.9545	2.38	0.9913
0.20	0.5793	0.70	0.7580	1.20	0.8849	1.70	0.9554	2.40	0.9918
0.21	0.5832	0.71	0.7611	1.21	0.8869	1.71	0.9564	2.42	0.9922
0.22	0.5871	0.72	0.7642	1.22	0.8888	1.72	0.9573	2.44	0.9927
0.23	0.5910	0.73	0.7673	1.23	0.8907	1.73	0.9582	2.46	0.9931
0.24	0.5948	0.74	0.7704	1.24	0.8925	1.74	0.9591	2.48	0.9934
0.25	0.5987	0.75	0.7734	1.25	0.8944	1.75	0.9599	2.50	0.9938
0.26	0.6026	0.76	0.7764	1.26	0.8962	1.76	0.9608	2.55	0.9946
0.27	0.6064	0.77	0.7794	1.27	0.8980	1.77	0.9616	2.60	0.9953
0.28	0.6103	0.78	0.7823	1.28	0.8997	1.78	0.9625	2.65	0.9960
0.29	0.6141	0.79	0.7852	1.29	0.9015	1.79	0.9633	2.70	0.9965
0.30	0.6179	0.80	0.7881	1.30	0.9032	1.80	0.9641	2.75	0.9970
0.31	0.6217	0.81	0.7910	1.31	0.9049	1.81	0.9649	2.80	0.9974
0.32	0.6255	0.82	0.7939	1.32	0.9066	1.82	0.9656	2.85	0.9978
0.33	0.6293	0.83	0.7967	1.33	0.9082	1.83	0.9664	2.90	0.9981
0.34	0.6331	0.84	0.7995	1.34	0.9099	1.84	0.9671	2.95	0.9984
0.35	0.6368	0.85	0.8023	1.35	0.9115	1.85	0.9678	3.00	0.9987
0.36	0.6406	0.86	0.8051	1.36	0.9131	1.86	0.9686	3.05	0.9989
0.37	0.6443	0.87	0.8078	1.37	0.9147	1.87	0.9693	3.10	0.9990
0.38	0.6480	0.88	0.8106	1.38	0.9162	1.88	0.9699	3.15	0.9992
0.39	0.6517	0.89	0.8133	1.39	0.9177	1.89	0.9706	3.20	0.9993
0.40	0.6554	0.90	0.8159	1.40	0.9192	1.90	0.9713	3.25	0.9994
0.41	0.6591	0.91	0.8186	1.41	0.9207	1.91	0.9719	3.30	0.9995
0.42	0.6628	0.92	0.8212	1.42	0.9222	1.92	0.9726	3.35	0.9996
0.43	0.6664	0.93	0.8238	1.43	0.9236	1.93	0.9732	3.40	0.9997
0.44	0.6700	0.94	0.8264	1.44	0.9251	1.94	0.9738	3.50	0.9998
0.45	0.6736	0.95	0.8289	1.45	0.9265	1.95	0.9744	3.60	0.9998
0.46	0.6772	0.96	0.8315	1.46	0.9279	1.96	0.9750	3.70	0.9999
0.47	0.6808	0.97	0.8340	1.47	0.9292	1.97	0.9756	3.80	0.9999
0.48	0.6844	0.98	0.8365	1.48	0.9306	1.98	0.9761	3.90	1.0000
0.49	0.6879	0.99	0.8389	1.49	0.9319	1.99	0.9767	4.00	1.0000

Percentage points of the normal distribution

The values z in the table are those which a random variable $Z \sim N(0,1)$ exceeds with probability p; that is, $P(Z > z) = p$.

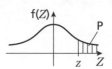

p	z	p	z
0.5000	0.0000	0.0500	1.6449
0.4000	0.2533	0.0250	1.9600
0.3000	0.5244	0.0100	2.3263
0.2000	0.8416	0.0050	2.5758
0.1500	1.0364	0.0010	3.0902
0.1000	1.2816	0.0005	3.2905

Answers

1 Data

1.1 Collecting and classifying data

1 a A list of the names of all the guests at the hotel.
  b It is much quicker to check the answers from a sample than from the whole population.
2 a A list of the names of all of the people in the Yorkshire Television area.
  b It is quicker and cheaper to take a sample rather than a census.
3 a A list of the names of all of the students whose papers are to be marked by the examiner.
  b The purpose is to check for consistency, not to mark every paper twice.
4 a A list of the names of the students at the university.
  b It is much quicker to check student preferences by taking a sample.
  c It is important to take a census when selecting someone to represent the population, for example, so that every person has a vote.
5 a Discrete. Shoe sizes can only take particular values. Half sizes are included but there are no quarter sizes for example.
  b Continuous. Foot length can take any value in a given range.
6 a Continuous
  b Discrete
7 Qualitative: B, E
  Discrete: A
  Continuous: C, D

8

Variable type	
Qualitative	**Quantitative**
	✓
✓	
	✓
	✓
✓	

9 a Primary data
  b Secondary data
  c Primary data

10

Data type	
Primary	**Secondary**
	✓
✓	
✓	
	✓
	✓

11 a Primary data
  b Using primary data will allow Kelly the necessary control over the way that the data is collected.

1.2 Calculating a stratified sample using two categories

1 Group size = 21
  Population size = 75
  Sample size = 20
  $\frac{21}{75} \times 20 = 6$(nearest whole number)
2 2
3 6
4 6
5 4

1.3 Petersen's capture and recapture method

1 a $M = 20 \qquad n = 21 \qquad m = 3$
  $N = \frac{20 \times 21}{3} = 140$
  b The reason for waiting two days is to allow time for the tagged fish to disperse evenly into the population.
2 a $\frac{100 \times 96}{4} = 2400$
  b 1 The tagged gannets disperse evenly into the population.
    2 The number of gannets remains fixed during the time between the samples being taken.
3 a $\frac{50 \times 40}{3} = 667$ to nearest whole number
  b Kerry mixed in the marked beads to make sure that they were evenly distributed within the jar.

Don't forget

* list
* represent
* every member
* specific values
* a given range
* measuring
* descriptions
* someone else
* proportion
* sample size
* estimated size
* captured, marked
* second
* previously marked
* disperses evenly
* size
* markers, tags
* equal chance

Exam-style questions

1 a A list of the names of people who live in the village.
  For parts **b** and **c** there are many possible answers. The ones given here are just examples.
  b A sample of people in the village might be asked for their views about the high-speed train line in order to judge the strength of feeling.
  c In the event of a strong response from a sample, a census might then be taken to demonstrate how the villagers feel.
2 a Qualitative
  b Continuous
3 $137 \times 40/(124 + 132 + 105 + 96 + 148 + 137)$
  = 7 (nearest whole number)
4 a $\frac{100 \times 75}{5} = 1500$
  b It would be very difficult to count so many fish as they move around.

2 Displaying data

2.1 Drawing diagrams

1

Boys			Girls
	15	7 7	
7	16	2 3 6 7 8 9 9	
9 7 6 5 2 0	17	0 1 2 8	
9 5 4 3 2 1 1 0	18	3	
3	19		

Key: 7 | 16 | 2 represents 167 cm for the boys and 162 cm for the girls.

2

			Paper 1			Paper 2			
		8	3	4	4	6	9		
9	9	8	5	1	5	0	2	5	7
9	8	6	4	3	2	6	0	1	3	4	8	8
	6	5	4	2	0	7	1	3	3	5	7
			7	2	8	0	2		

Key: 3 | 4 | 6 represents a mark of 43 on Paper 1 and
46 on Paper 2

3

		Ponies				Horses				
	3	2	1	0	12					
3	2	2	1	0	13					
3	2	2	1	1	14	2	2	3	3	3
					15	0	1	3	3	
					16	1	1	2	2	3

Key: 1 | 14 | 2 represents 14.1 hands for the ponies and 14.2
hands for the horses.

4

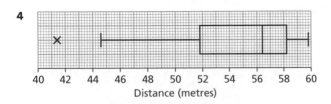

5

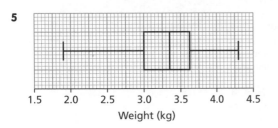

6

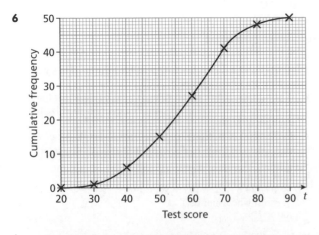

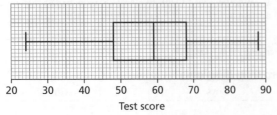

7

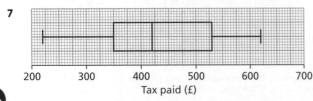

8

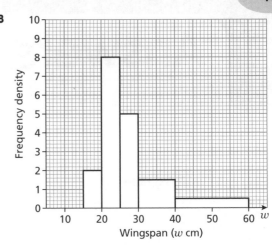

9

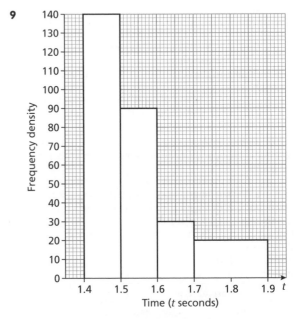

10

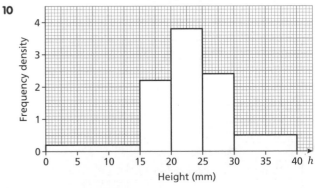

11

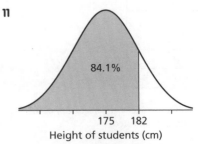
84.1%
175   182
Height of students (cm)

12
97.7%
216.3   216.5
Lengths of rails (cm)

13

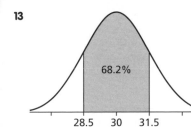

14

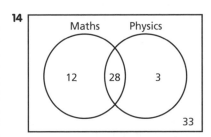

15

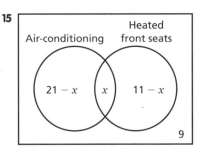

The number of cars with heated front seats only is $11 - x$
The total number of cars in the circles is 26
$21 - x + x + 11 - x = 26$
$x = 6$

16

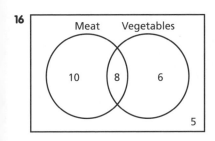

Don't forget

* compare
* minimum, maximum
* frequency density
* mean
* sample space

Exam-style questions

1

Petrol					Diesel				
	8	7	5	8					
6	6	4	4	3	9	6	8		
6	6	2	2	0	10	1	7	7	8
				1	11	0	2	4	8	9
					12	2	5	6	

2

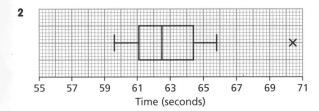

3

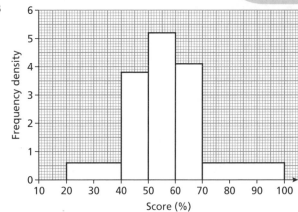

4

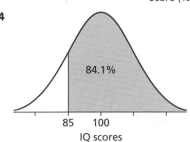

5

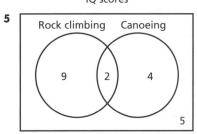

3 Calculating with data

3.1 Means and index numbers

1 **a** $\sqrt{900} = 30$ **b** 12
2 125.6
3 134.4
4 **a** -10 **b** $224 - 232 = -8$
    c $\dfrac{-10 + -8}{2} = -9$
5 **a** $-13\,000$ **b** $-15\,000$
    c $-14\,000$ (make allowance for reading from graph)
6 **a** 104.0   **b** 103.3
    c From January 2011 to January 2012 the cost rose by 4.0%
    From January 2012 to January 2013 the cost rose by 3.3%
    The percentage increase was greater from January 2011 to
    January 2012 than from January 2012 to January 2013.
7 **a** 104   **b** 105.0
    c The price rose by 4% from 2011 to 2012
    The price rose by 5.0% from 2012 to 2013
    The percentage increase was greater from 2012 to 2013 than
    from 2011 to 2012.
8 **a** 106.2   **b** 106
    c From June 2011 to June 2012 the price increased by 6.2%
    From June 2012 to June 2013 the price increased by 6%
    The percentage increase was slightly greater from June 2011
    to June 2012 than from June 2012 to June 2013.

3.2 Mean and standard deviation for grouped and ungrouped data

1 $\Sigma fx = 184$ $\Sigma fx^2 = 808$ $\dfrac{808}{50} - \left(\dfrac{184}{50}\right)^2 = 2.6176$
standard deviation = 1.62
2 $\Sigma fx = 10\,660$ $\dfrac{\Sigma fx}{\Sigma f} = \dfrac{10\,660}{60} = 177.66\ldots$
An estimate of the mean is 177.7 to 1 d.p.
$\Sigma fx^2 = 1\,895\,525$ $\dfrac{1\,895\,525}{60} - \left(\dfrac{10\,660}{60}\right)^2 = 26.638\ldots$
An estimate of the standard deviation = 5.2
3 **a** mean = 2.43
    b standard deviation = 1.38

4 a 3   **b** 1.97
5 a 4.975   **b** 1.17

3.3 Outliers

1 $Q1 = 27$ $3\dfrac{(11+1)}{4} = 9$ $Q3 = 35$ $IQR = 8$
$Q3 + 1.5 \times IQR = 47$ $Q1 - 1.5 \times IQR = 15$
The value 52 is an outlier.

2 a 16
   b 16, 17, 83

3 $Q1 = 38$ $Q3 = 51$ $IQR = 13$
$Q1 - 1.5 \times IQR = 18.5 > 18$
$Q3 + 1.5 \times IQR = 70.5 < 72$

3.4 Measures of correlation

1 a $\Sigma d^2 = 16$ $1 - \dfrac{6 \times 16}{8(8^2 - 1)} = 0.810$ (3 d.p.)

2 0.745
3 0.952
4 $S_{xy} = 12\,703 - \dfrac{237 \times 457}{10} = 1872.1$
$r = \dfrac{1872.1}{\sqrt{5698.1 \times 672.1}} = 0.957$

5 0.71
6 0.71

3.5 Calculation of S_{xx}, S_{yy} and S_{xy}

1 a $S_{xy} = 355.09 - \dfrac{54.5^2}{10} = 58.065$

   b $126.25 - \dfrac{32.5^2}{10} = 20.625$

   c $211.7 - \dfrac{32.5 \times 54.5}{10} = 34.575$

2 a 2062.5   **b** 15 504.4   **c** −4575
3 0.996 (3 d.p.)

3.6 Calculation of standardised scores

1 $\dfrac{78 - 55}{10.5} = 2.190 \ldots = 2.2$ (1 d.p.)
2 −1.67 (2 d.p.)
3 2.03 (2 d.p.)

Don't forget

* $\sqrt[4]{abcd}$
* best fit
* trend line
* fx^2
* mid-point
* upper quartile
* lower quartile
* d
* S_{xy}
* Mean

Exam-style questions

1 a 105.5
   b 117.6
2 a 3.93
   b 2.62
3 $Q1 = 19$, $Q3 = 30$, $IQR = 11$
$30 + 1.5 \times 11 = 46.5 > 41$
41 is not an outlier.
4 0.738 (3 d.p.)
5 $\dfrac{694.333}{\sqrt{1357.7 \times 1938.7}} = 0.428$
6 −217
7 Tim. Alison's standardised score is $1.03 < 1.2$

4 Interpreting data

4.1 Compare histograms and normal distributions

1 1 The modal class interval for Andy's serves is 90–100 mph.
    The modal class interval for Roger's serves is 120–130 mph.
   2 The speeds of Andy's serves have a positive skew.
    The speeds of Roger's serves have no skew.
   3 Roger has a higher proportion of serves greater than
    120 mph than Andy.

2 1 The modal class interval for the females is 30–35 kg.
    The modal class interval for the males is 40–45 kg.
   2 The weights of the females have positive skew.
    The weights of the males have negative skew.
   3 A much higher proportion of the males weigh more than
    40 kg compared with the females.
3 1 The modal class interval for Year 7 is 4–6 hours.
    The modal class interval for Year 11 is 6–8 hours.
   2 The Year 7 times have a slight positive skew.
    The Year 11 times have a slight negative skew.
   3 A higher proportion of Year 11 students spend more than
    6 hours on their homework compared with Year 7 students.
4 1 Group A has a lower mean cholesterol level than Group B.
   2 Group A has a higher standard deviation than Group B.
5 1 The mean length is reduced slightly.
   2 The standard deviation is significantly reduced, making the
    lengths more consistent.

4.2 Identify and describe correlation in scatter graphs and interpret measures of correlation

1 a Positive
   b 0.858 (3 d.p.)
   c Strong positive correlation
2 a Negative
   b −0.685
   c Strong negative correlation

4.3 Identify trend and seasonality in time-series graphs

1 a 37.5 $\dfrac{41 + 27 + 35 + 55}{4} = 39.5$

$\dfrac{27 + 35 + 55 + 49}{4} = 41.5$

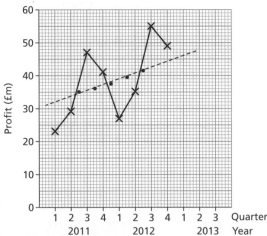

   b $(-9 + -12)/2 = -10.5$
   c $46 - 10.5 = 35.5$
    Predicted profit = £35.5m
2 a 24.5, 25.5, 26
   b

   c $(5 + 6)/2 = 5.5$
   d Using the mean seasonal variation gives a predicted value of
    29 000 + 5500 = 34 500 so the prediction of 30 000 seems
    too low.

3 a

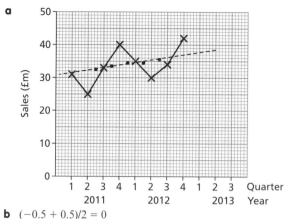

b $(-0.5 + 0.5)/2 = 0$

c £38m The prediction should be quite accurate since it is for the quarter immediately following the given information and the 4-point moving averages lie close to a straight line.

4.4 Interpret and compare data

1 2012: $100 + 320 + 240 + 140 = 800$
2013: $120 + 340 + 200 + 300 = 960$
960 runners took part in 2013 compared with 800 in 2012.

2 a Median for Paper 1 is 61%
Median for Paper 2 is 63%

b IQR for Paper 1 is $69 - 53 = 16$
IQR for Paper 2 is $71 - 54 = 17$

c Number who scored 60% or less on Paper 1 is 22
Number who scored 60% or less on Paper 2 is 19

3 a Sandon: Median = 17
Stafford: Median = 42

b Sandon: IQR = $27 - 10 = 17$
Stafford: IQR = $54 - 24 = 30$

c Sandon: Positive skew
Stafford: Negative skew

4 1 The median battery life is 32 minutes after 2 years compared with 96 minutes after 1 year.

2 The IQR after 2 years is 26 minutes which is the same as it was after 1 year.

3 The shortest battery life after 2 years is 2 minutes compared with 72 minutes after 1 year.

5 Nathan's standardised score is $1.14 > 0.84$
Nathan performed better than Lisa on the test.

6 Philip's standardised score in Maths is 1.33
Philip's standardised score in Biology is 0.9
Philip performed better in Maths.

7 a Carl Lewis: -2.34
Usain Bolt: -0.64

b Carl Lewis was faster in relation to the other finalists in 1984 than Usain Bolt was in relation to the other finalists in 2012.

c New standardised time for Usain Bolt is -1.75

d The new standardised time for Usain Bolt is improved by removing the outlier, but Carl Lewis still has a better standardised time.

4.5 Geometric means and chain base index numbers

1 a

Year	2011	2012	2013
Index number	105.2	103.8	107.5

An increase of 5.2% gives a base index of $100 + 5.2 = 105.2$

b 105.5

c The geometric mean is equivalent to a 5.5% increase.

2 a

Year	2009	2010	2011	2012
Index number	116.2	109.6	109.5	105.6

b 110.2

c Kevin's heating costs have gone up by $10.2\% < 11\%$ so Jill's heating costs have gone up more.

3 a

Year	2011	2012	2013
Index number	106.8	104.4	110.6

b 107.2   **c** 7.2%

4 a

Year	2009	2010	2011	2012	2013
Index number	82.4	65.1	62.6	60.0	53.9

b 64.1

c 35.9% reduction compared with 2008

4.6 Interpreting diagrams

1 a Median for the boys is 65 compared with 63 for the girls.

b The IQR for the boys is 21 compared with 16 for the girls.

2 a The median weight of the apples is 156 grams compared with 183 grams for the oranges.

3 a The median milk yield for the Holstein cows is 27 litres compared with 21 litres for the Jersey cows.

4 a 23 minutes   **b** 29 minutes

5 a 6 seconds

b

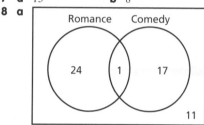

6 a 33 minutes   **b** 52.5 minutes

c $42.5 + 1.5 \times 5.5 = 50.75 < 52.5$

7 a 13   **b** 8

8 a

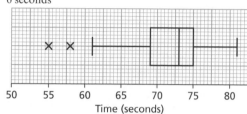

b 17

Don't forget

* positive
* negative
* previous
* chain
* same
* percentage
* comparison
* same
* outliers
* facts

Exam-style questions

1 a Positive

b 0.943 (3 d.p.)

c Strong positive correlation.

2 a

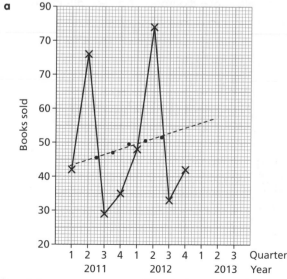

b -1.5 **c** 55 books (approximately)

3 a Buxton standardised time: -1.3 minutes
Macclesfield standardised time: -1.42

b Ron performed better in relation to the other competitors in the Macclesfield triathlon than he did in relation to the other competitors in the Buxton triathlon.

4 a

Year	2011	2012	2013
Index number	129.2	110.4	140.6

b 126.1

c The geometric mean indicates a 26.1% increase.

5 a 1 The median number of visitors in September was 800 compared with 2450 in August.
2 The highest number of visitors in September was 1850 compared with 3450 in August.

Other comparisons could be made, such as the interquartile ranges.

b IQR for September $= 650$ Q3 for September $= 1300$
$1300 + 1.5 \times 650 = 2275 < 2800$ so 2800 is an outlier.

c

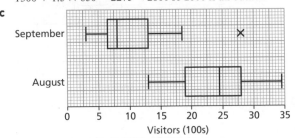

5 Probability

5.1 Probability and relative frequency

1 22

2 a 0.2235
b 45

3 a 0.65
b Increase the number of trials

4

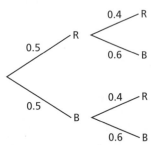

a 0.3
b 6

5.2 Sample space diagrams and Venn diagrams

1 a

		First spinner			
		1	2	3	4
Second spinner	1	2	3	4	5
	2	3	4	5	6
	3	4	5	6	7
	4	5	6	7	8

b $\frac{3}{16}$

2 HHH
HHT
HTH
THH
TTH
THT
HTT
TTT
$\frac{1}{2}$

3 a

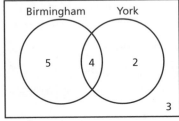

b $\frac{15}{36} = \frac{5}{12}$

c $\frac{21}{36} = \frac{7}{12}$

4 $9 + 3 = 12$
$2 + 3 + 9 + 2 + 6 + 11 = 33$
$\frac{12}{33} = \frac{4}{11}$

5 a

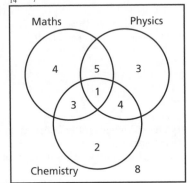

b $\frac{4}{14} = \frac{2}{7}$

6 a

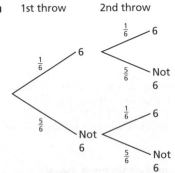

b $\frac{5}{30} = \frac{1}{6}$

5.3 Tree diagrams

1 a   1st throw   2nd throw

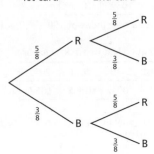

b $\frac{1}{36}$

c $\frac{10}{36} = \frac{5}{18}$

2 a   1st card   2nd card

b $\frac{15}{64}$

c $\frac{34}{64} = \frac{17}{32}$

3 a

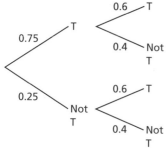

Alice   Bob

0.75 — T
0.6 — T
0.4 — Not T

0.25 — Not T
0.6 — T
0.4 — Not T

b 0.9

5.4 Mutually exclusive events

1 $\frac{3}{6}, \frac{1}{6}$, 3, mutually exclusive, $\frac{3}{6} + \frac{1}{6} = \frac{4}{6} = \frac{2}{3}$

2 0.59

3 0.49

4 $\frac{17}{24}$

5 $0.39 + 0.52 \neq 0.76$ so $P(X \text{ or } Y) \neq P(X) + P(Y)$

6 a $\frac{8}{11}$ **b** $\frac{3}{11}$

5.5 Combined events

1 $\frac{1}{2} \times \frac{1}{2} = \frac{1}{4}$

2 $P(TTT) = P(T) \times P(T) \times P(T) = \frac{1}{2} \times \frac{1}{2} \times \frac{1}{2} = \frac{1}{8}$

3 $\frac{12}{125}$

4 $\frac{2}{3} \times \frac{3}{4} = \frac{1}{2} \neq \frac{5}{12}$ so $P(X) \times P(Y) \neq P(X \cap Y)$

5 $\frac{16}{49}$

6 $0.3 + 0.6 - 0.3 \times 0.6 = 0.72$

7 $\frac{3}{10}, \frac{5}{10}, \frac{1}{10}$

$\frac{3}{10} + \frac{5}{10} - \frac{1}{10} = \frac{7}{10}$

8 $0.7 + 0.8 - 0.6 = 0.9$

9 $0.3 + 0.25 - 0.3 \times 0.25 = 0.475$

5.6 Conditional probabilities

1 a $\frac{4}{10} \times \frac{3}{9} = \frac{12}{90} = \frac{2}{15}$

   b $\frac{4}{10} \times \frac{6}{9} + \frac{6}{10} \times \frac{4}{9} = \frac{48}{90} = \frac{8}{15}$

2 a $0.5 \times 0.6 = 0.3$

   b $0.5 \times 0.4 + 0.5 \times 0.4 = 0.4$

3 $\frac{1}{52}, \frac{1}{4}, \frac{1}{13}$

4 a $\frac{110}{320} = \frac{11}{32}$ **b** $\frac{50}{110} = \frac{5}{11}$

5 a $\frac{10}{160} = \frac{1}{16}$ **b** $\frac{10}{76} = \frac{5}{38}$

5.7 Binomial probabilities

1 a $n = 6$

$p = 0.43$ so $1 - p = 0.57$

$r = 2$

$P(\text{two Heads}) = {}^6C_2 \times 0.43^2 \times 0.57^4 = 0.2927\ldots$

$= 0.293$ (3 d.p.)

   b $P(0 \text{ Heads}) = 0.57^6 = 0.03429\ldots$

$P(\text{at least one Head}) = 1 - 0.03429\ldots$

$= 0.966$ (3 d.p.)

2 a 0.219

   b 0.996

3 a 0.250

   b 0.944

5.8 The normal distribution

1 a $P(Z < \frac{55 - 50}{12}) = P(Z < 0.42) = \Phi(0.42) = 0.6628$

   b $P(X > 70) = P(Z > \frac{70 - 50}{12}) = P(Z > 1.67)$

$= 1 - P(Z < 1.67)$

$= 1 - \Phi(1.67)$

$= 0.0475$

   c $P(X < 35) = P(Z < \frac{35 - 50}{12})$

$= 1 - \Phi(1.25) = 0.1056$

2 a 0.9834

   b 0.2119

   c 0.1151

3 a 0.0314

   b 63

Don't forget

* $P(A) \times n$
* event
* multiply
* add
* outcomes
* happen
* $P(A) + P(B)$
* $P(A \cup B)$
* does not affect
* $P(A) \times P(B)$
* $P(A \cap B)$
* both
* $P(A) + P(B) - P(A \cap B)$
* 0
* $P(A) + P(B)$
* $P(A)$
* $\dfrac{P(A \cap B)}{P(A)}$
* fixed
* same each time
* independent
* $\dfrac{n!}{r!(n - r)!}$
* $^nC_r p^r (1 - p)^{n - r}$
* $\dfrac{X - \mu}{\sigma}$
* $P(Z < z)$
* $(Z < z)$
* $\Phi(z)$
* $1 - \Phi(z)$

Exam-style questions

1 a

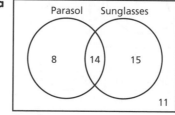

Parasol   Sunglasses

8   14   15

11

   b $\frac{14}{22} = \frac{7}{11}$

2 0.58

3 0.72

4 a 0.472   **b** 0.75

5 a   First crayon   Second crayon

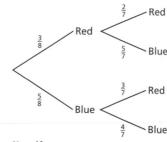

Red $\frac{3}{8}$
$\frac{2}{7}$ Red
$\frac{5}{7}$ Blue

Blue $\frac{5}{8}$
$\frac{3}{7}$ Red
$\frac{4}{7}$ Blue

   b $\frac{30}{56} = \frac{15}{28}$

6 a 0.194 (3 d.p.)   **b** 0.972 (3 d.p.)

7 a 29.5   **b** 0.8849   **c** 0.837

Practice Paper

1 a A list of the names of the students in the school

   b It is quicker to administer.

2 a $Q3 + 1.5 \times IQR = £525 + 1.5 \times £60 = £615 < £648$

so £648 is an outlier.

   b

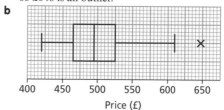

400   450   500   550   600   650

Price (£)

3 a

First test		Second test
9 8 7 5 3 2	4	7 8
8 6 5 5 3 1 1 0	5	0 3 5 6 9
8 8 8 6 6 4 4 3 3	6	1 3 4 5 6 7 7 7 7 7 8 9
8 8 6 5 2 2 0	7	1 2 2 2 4 5 6 7 8
	8	0 3

b 1 The median mark on the first test is 63 compared with 67 on the second test.
    2 The range on the first test is 36 which is the same as on the second test.

4 a First match   Second match

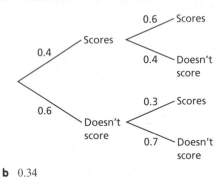

b 0.34
5 a 0.04   **b** 0.37   **c** 0.16   **d** 0.229 (3 d.p.)
6 2.17 (2 d.p.)
7 a

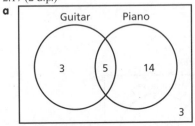

b $\frac{5}{19}$

8 a

Year	2010	2011	2012	2013
Index number	103.9	110.7	119.7	138.2

b 117.4
c An increase of 17.4% per year.
9 a

b 41

10 2
11 a 0.857
   b Strong positive correlation.
     0.857 > 0.5
12 a 360
   b 1 Make sure that the tags cannot be removed by the squirrels.
      2 Allow sufficient time for the tagged squirrels to disperse into the population.
13 a 50, 52, 53

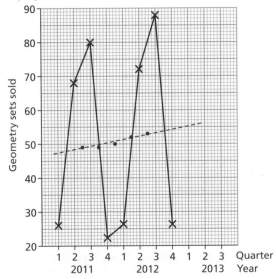

b −23.5
c 31 (approximately)
14 1 The median time per paper for 200 papers is 22 minutes which is much less than 39 minutes which is the median for the first 20 papers.
   2 The times for the first 20 papers have a negative skew whereas the times for the 200 papers have a slight positive skew.
   3 The interquartile range for the 200 papers is 13 minutes compared with 18 minutes for the first 20 papers.
15 a Alice's standardised score = 0.429 (3 d.p.)
     Bob's standardised score = 0.75
   b Bob performed better compared with the other students who took the Mechanics paper than Alice did compared with the other students who took the Statistics paper.
16 1 The pies from Supplier B have a higher median weight than the pies from Supplier A.
   2 The pies from Supplier B have a more consistent weight than the pies from Supplier A.
17 $\frac{26}{56} = \frac{13}{28}$
18 a 0.9554
   b 0.7257
   c 0.1129
19 a −1661.4
   b −0.974 (3 d.p.)
20 a 0.402 (3 d.p.)
   b 0.196 (3 d.p.)
   c 6